...HER & HIGHER EDUCATIC

SYSTEMS OF LIFE

VOLUME I

1

Anne Roberts and Peter Gardiner

First edition 1992
Reprinted 1993,1994

Published by
MACMILLAN MAGAZINES LTD
4 Little Essex Street
London WC2R 3LF

Companies and representatives throughout the world
Printed in Great Britain by
Prolitho
London

ISBN 0-333-57860-8

CONTENTS

INTRODUCTION

Systems of Life started to appear regularly in *Nursing Times* in 1975 and has become a firm favourite with generations of nurses, nursing students and their teachers.

It proves, perhaps, that the simple ideas are usually the best. The clear illustrations and uncluttered text give an attractive, accessible and authoritative guide to anatomy and physiology. Systems of Life represents all the elements of *Nursing Times* that make the journal so well respected — it combines good design with well-written material and appears regularly and reliably.

Simplicity is deceptive, however, and I doubt whether many people outside the *Nursing Times* office realise quite how much time and effort goes into researching, producing and checking the monthly features. Therefore, this introduction represents a welcome chance to pay tribute to the professionalism of the Systems of Life team — desk editor, Jean Cullinan, illustrator, Peter Gardiner, and writer, Anne Roberts. I hope admirers of Systems of Life — and those encountering it for the first time — will use, enjoy and treasure this collection of their work.

John Gilbert
Editor, *Nursing Times*

SYSTEMS OF LIFE
The cardiovascular system Part I

The cardiovascular system consists of the heart and blood vessels — arteries
— veins
— capillaries.

It forms a transport system for oxygen, nutrients, waste products, hormones and antibodies within the body.

The heart muscle itself is called the <u>myocardium</u> and the smooth endothelial lining of the cavities is the <u>endocardium</u>.

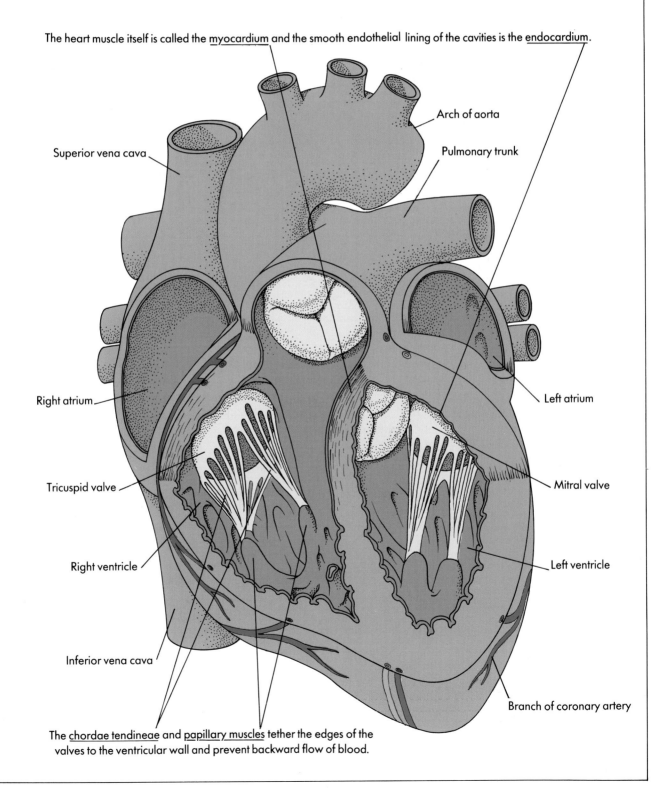

Superior vena cava

Arch of aorta

Pulmonary trunk

Right atrium

Left atrium

Tricuspid valve

Mitral valve

Right ventricle

Left ventricle

Inferior vena cava

Branch of coronary artery

The <u>chordae tendineae</u> and <u>papillary muscles</u> tether the edges of the valves to the ventricular wall and prevent backward flow of blood.

Surface anatomy

The heart is about the size of its owner's clenched fist. It lies in the centre of the thoracic cavity, behind the sternum and in front of the descending aorta and oesophagus.

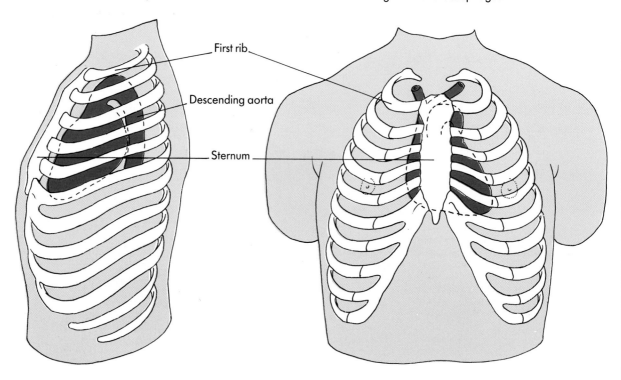

First rib

Descending aorta

Sternum

The base points upwards, backwards and to the right, and the apex downwards, forwards and to the left.

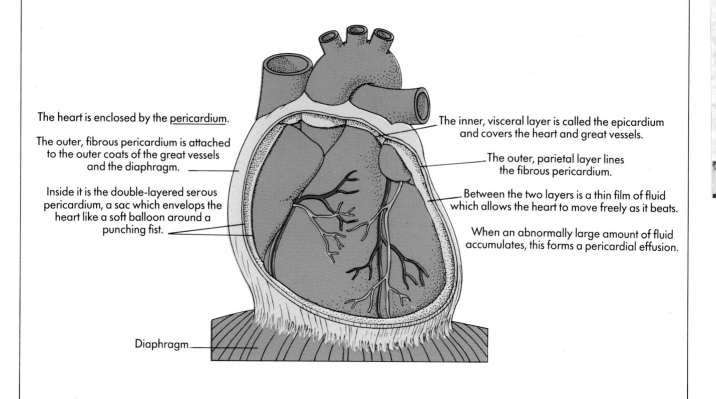

The heart is enclosed by the <u>pericardium</u>.

The outer, fibrous pericardium is attached to the outer coats of the great vessels and the diaphragm.

Inside it is the double-layered serous pericardium, a sac which envelops the heart like a soft balloon around a punching fist.

The inner, visceral layer is called the epicardium and covers the heart and great vessels.

The outer, parietal layer lines the fibrous pericardium.

Between the two layers is a thin film of fluid which allows the heart to move freely as it beats.

When an abnormally large amount of fluid accumulates, this forms a pericardial effusion.

Diaphragm

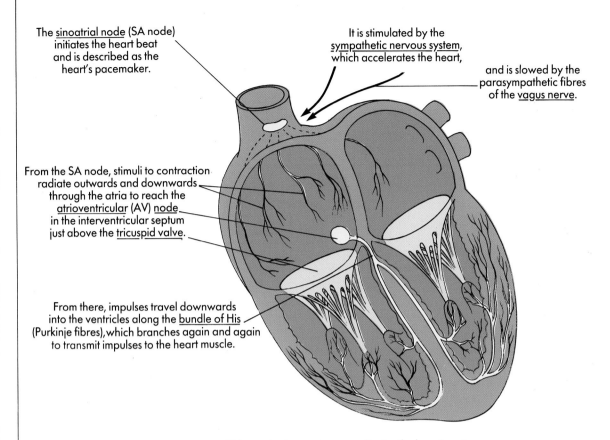

The sinoatrial node (SA node) initiates the heart beat and is described as the heart's pacemaker.

It is stimulated by the sympathetic nervous system, which accelerates the heart,

and is slowed by the parasympathetic fibres of the vagus nerve.

From the SA node, stimuli to contraction radiate outwards and downwards through the atria to reach the atrioventricular (AV) node in the interventricular septum just above the tricuspid valve.

From there, impulses travel downwards into the ventricles along the bundle of His (Purkinje fibres), which branches again and again to transmit impulses to the heart muscle.

This conduction system co-ordinates the heart's action.

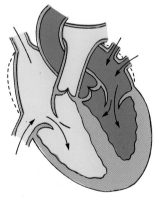
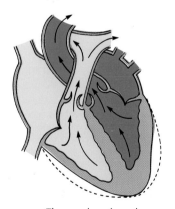
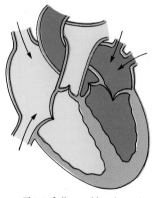

The two atria contract together (atrial systole), squeezing their blood through the mitral and tricuspid valves into the ventricles.

These valves then close, and the two ventricles contract together, squeezing their blood into the great vessels (pulmonary trunk and aorta) — ventricular systole.

This is followed by diastole, when the relaxed heart fills with blood again.

The electrical changes that take place during the cardiac cycle can be recorded as the electrocardiogram (ECG).

The pattern is altered by disease, so that ECG is useful in diagnosis.

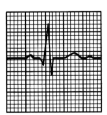

When the conduction system becomes faulty, an artificial 'pacemaker' wire connected to an external battery can be inserted to keep the heart beating effectively.

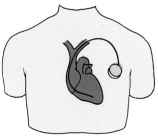

Blood vessels

Arteries carry blood away from the heart, and all except the pulmonary artery carry oxygenated blood.
Arterial blood is at a higher pressure than that on the venous side of the circulation.

Arteries have thick walls and three layers:
— tunica intima, a lining layer of smooth endothelium
— tunica media, the middle, thickest layer, made up of
    smooth muscle and elastic tissue.
— tunica adventitia, an outer layer of collagen fibres which merge
    with the surrounding connective tissue.

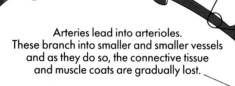

Arteries lead into arterioles.
These branch into smaller and smaller vessels
and as they do so, the connective tissue
and muscle coats are gradually lost.

The remaining branching tubes of
endothelium form the capillary bed.
The capillaries have thin permeable walls
through which the tissues obtain
oxygen and nutrients and pass back
carbon dioxide and waste products.

The capillaries join up to form venules
which in turn unite to form veins.
Veins carry blood towards the heart.
Except for that in the pulmonary veins,
the blood they carry is dark and deoxygenated.

The veins join up so that they are larger in size
but fewer in number. Eventually the superior
and inferior venae cavae are formed,
draining into the right atrium.

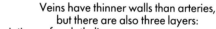

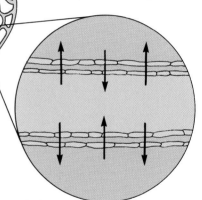

Veins have thinner walls than arteries,
but there are also three layers:
— tunica intima, of endothelium
— tunica media, which has little muscle or elastic tissue but contains
    a lot of collagen; this makes the wall very strong.
— tunica adventitia, with muscle and elastic fibres

The larger vessels also have their own
blood vessels (vasa vasorum) and lymphatics,
running in the adventitia.

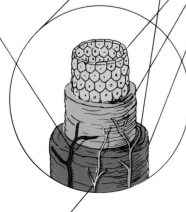

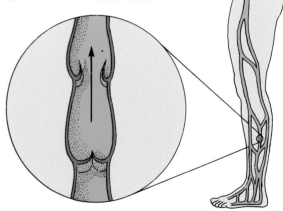

Vasomotor nerves constrict and relax the muscle
in the blood vessel walls. This alters the amount of blood
that flows through the vessels, their resistance to the
flow and the quantity of blood that they hold at any one time.

Veins over about 2mm in diameter have valves shaped like pockets
with the free edge towards the heart. When blood flows as it should,
towards the heart, the valves lie flat against the vein walls.
However, if it starts to flow backwards, the pockets fill up and block
the lumen of the vein, effectively preventing further backward flow.

SYSTEMS OF LIFE
The cardiovascular system Part II

The circulation of the blood

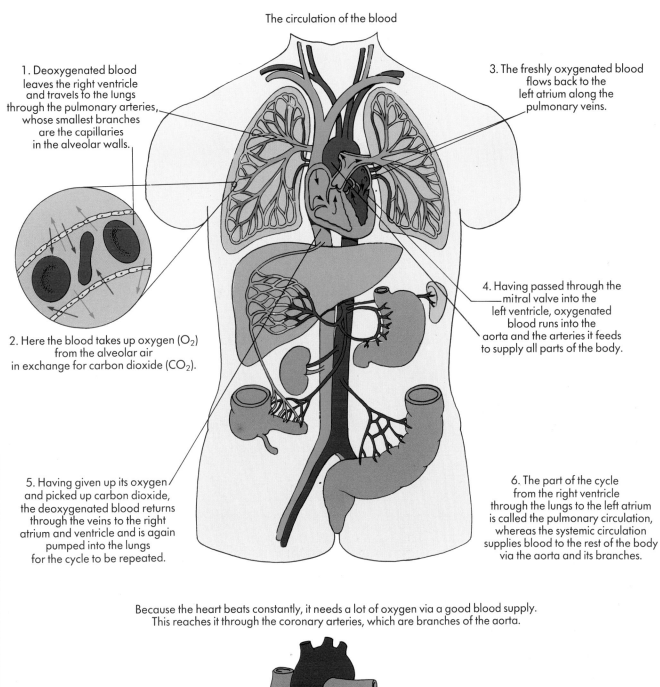

1. Deoxygenated blood leaves the right ventricle and travels to the lungs through the pulmonary arteries, whose smallest branches are the capillaries in the alveolar walls.

2. Here the blood takes up oxygen (O_2) from the alveolar air in exchange for carbon dioxide (CO_2).

3. The freshly oxygenated blood flows back to the left atrium along the pulmonary veins.

4. Having passed through the mitral valve into the left ventricle, oxygenated blood runs into the aorta and the arteries it feeds to supply all parts of the body.

5. Having given up its oxygen and picked up carbon dioxide, the deoxygenated blood returns through the veins to the right atrium and ventricle and is again pumped into the lungs for the cycle to be repeated.

6. The part of the cycle from the right ventricle through the lungs to the left atrium is called the pulmonary circulation, whereas the systemic circulation supplies blood to the rest of the body via the aorta and its branches.

Because the heart beats constantly, it needs a lot of oxygen via a good blood supply.
This reaches it through the coronary arteries, which are branches of the aorta.

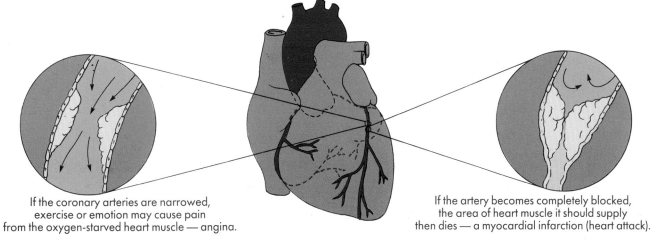

If the coronary arteries are narrowed, exercise or emotion may cause pain from the oxygen-starved heart muscle — angina.

If the artery becomes completely blocked, the area of heart muscle it should supply then dies — a myocardial infarction (heart attack).

The fetal circulation

Before birth the baby in the uterus receives its nutrients and oxygen from the mother's blood via the placenta, where gas exchange takes place between maternal and fetal blood.

1. Oxygenated blood passes from the placenta along the umbilical vein to reach the fetus.

4. A small amount of right atrial blood enters the pulmonary trunk. Most of this is short circuited through the ductus arteriosus to the aorta, but a little goes to the lungs. During fetal life these are unexpanded and only need enough blood for their own tissue requirements, rather than the large amount needed to carry oxygen in postnatal life.

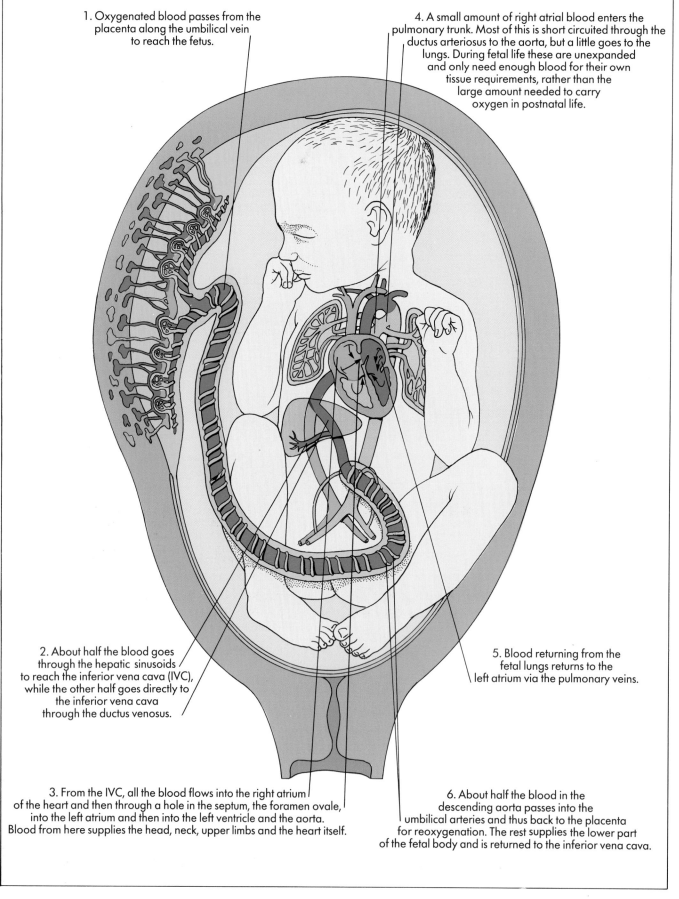

2. About half the blood goes through the hepatic sinusoids to reach the inferior vena cava (IVC), while the other half goes directly to the inferior vena cava through the ductus venosus.

5. Blood returning from the fetal lungs returns to the left atrium via the pulmonary veins.

3. From the IVC, all the blood flows into the right atrium of the heart and then through a hole in the septum, the foramen ovale, into the left atrium and then into the left ventricle and the aorta. Blood from here supplies the head, neck, upper limbs and the heart itself.

6. About half the blood in the descending aorta passes into the umbilical arteries and thus back to the placenta for reoxygenation. The rest supplies the lower part of the fetal body and is returned to the inferior vena cava.

SYSTEMS OF LIFE

Changes at birth
At birth the baby's lungs take over from the maternal placenta as the supplier of oxygen.

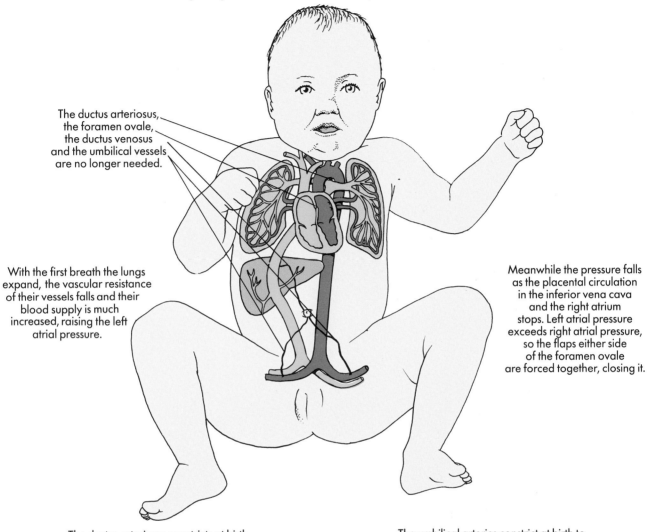

The ductus arteriosus, the foramen ovale, the ductus venosus and the umbilical vessels are no longer needed.

With the first breath the lungs expand, the vascular resistance of their vessels falls and their blood supply is much increased, raising the left atrial pressure.

Meanwhile the pressure falls as the placental circulation in the inferior vena cava and the right atrium stops. Left atrial pressure exceeds right atrial pressure, so the flaps either side of the foramen ovale are forced together, closing it.

The ductus arteriosus constricts at birth and closes gradually in infancy. It is usually obliterated by the end of the third month.

The umbilical arteries constrict at birth to prevent loss of the baby's blood. The umbilical vein remains patent for some time, and can if necessary be used for exchange transfusions in the newborn baby.

Congenital heart disease

Some types happen because the developing heart is malformed during embryonic life (eg because of rubella infection). Others occur because of failure or delay of fetal circulation to change to the adult pattern.

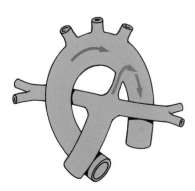

Patent ductus arteriosus

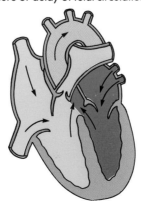

Tetralogy of Fallot

Truncus arteriosus

For instance, a patent ductus arteriosus is found in premature babies or those with persistent hypoxia (low blood oxygen level), as well as in fetal rubella victims. Some cases respond to treatment with the drug indomethacin; others require surgery.

SYSTEMS OF LIFE

Nursing observations of the cardiovascular system

(a) The pulse

The radial pulse at the wrist is most commonly taken.
The rate and rhythm are recorded.

Rate
This is very variable; usually 60–100/min in adults.

Increased (fast rate is tachycardia):
— by exercise
— by nervousness
— in some illnesses eg thyrotoxicosis, anaemia, cardiac failure,
                  acute haemorrhage.

Decreased (slow rate is bradycardia)
— in trained athletes
— in some illnesses eg heartblock, myxoedema, raised intracranial
                pressure, obstructive jaundice.

Rhythm may also be noted,

whether — regular
          — irregular — completely irregular
                    — with a recurring pattern of irregularity
                    — occasional irregularity

The following pulses can also be felt:
— superficial temporal
— carotid
— brachial
— femoral
— popliteal
— posterior tibial
— dorsalis pedis

Pulse strength may indicate the amount of blood flow. If an artery is narrowed,
pulses below the blockage will be less strong and more difficult to feel.

(b) The blood pressure (BP)

This is measured because:
1. The amount of blood reaching the tissues depends on the pressure at which it is delivered;
if BP is too low — for instance after a haemorrhage — blood supply may be insufficient
for tissue needs, so organs such as the kidneys become damaged.
2. Too high a BP is associated with diseases such as stroke.

How to take the blood pressure.

This is done with a sphygmomanometer. The inflatable cuff bag should be long
enough to encircle the arm, with its centre over the brachial artery, which can be
identified in the antecubital fossa (front of elbow). The systolic pressure by
palpation (feeling) can be found if the cuff is inflated and then deflated until the
radial pulse just appears. Then, with the stethoscope bell over the brachial artery
the cuff is inflated to about 30mm above the systolic pressure by palpation. The
cuff is then deflated slowly to the level at which two successive beats are heard;
this is the systolic pressure by auscultation (listening). As the pressure is further
lowered, the sounds become loud and banging. The point where they suddenly
become muffled ('4th phase') is usually recorded as the diastolic pressure, though
'5th phase' (disappearance of sounds) is sometimes used. The BP may then be
recorded on a chart, or written in the form:— $\frac{\text{systolic}}{\text{diastolic}}$ mmHg

Effect of poor cardiovascular function on the activities of daily living

1. A patient in heart failure will find breathing easier
and sleeping more comfortable if he is
propped in a semi-sitting position.

2. Mobility, work and self care may be limited by shortness
of breath, angina on exertion or leg pain
from peripheral vascular disease.

3. Someone with recurrent attacks of severe angina
may feel safer if he has a telephone or a body-worn alarm.

4. Sexual activity may bring on angina,
and anxiety may cause impotence.
Discussion, reassurance and treatment when necessary can help.

SYSTEMS OF LIFE
The respiratory system Part I

The purpose of the respiratory system is to provide the oxygen that is needed for all body processes, and to dispose of the waste product carbon dioxide.

It consists of: (1) The nose, mouth and pharynx, (2) The larynx, (3) The trachea, (4) The bronchi; these together form the airway. (5) The alveoli and the alveolar ducts joining them to the smallest bronchi form the substance of the (6) lungs, which are enclosed by the (7) pleura. The whole is controlled by the respiratory centre (8).

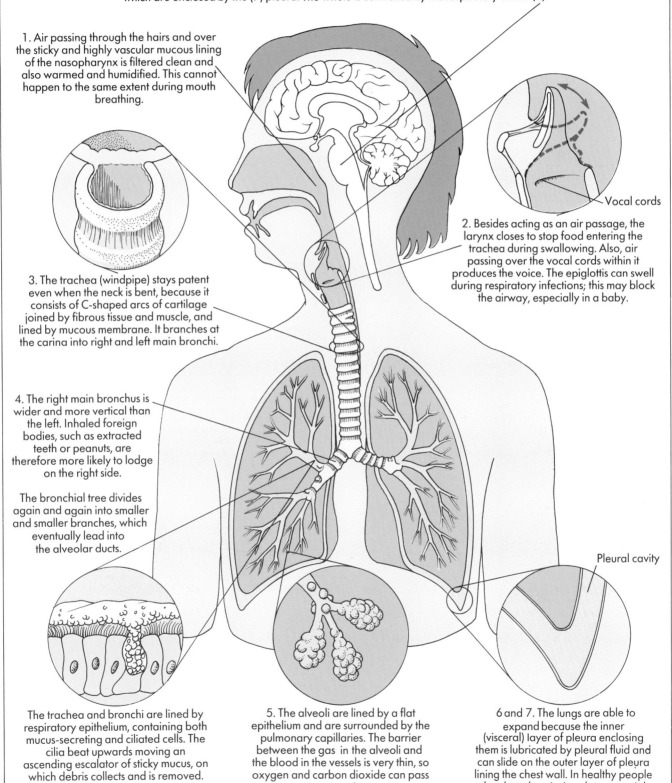

1. Air passing through the hairs and over the sticky and highly vascular mucous lining of the nasopharynx is filtered clean and also warmed and humidified. This cannot happen to the same extent during mouth breathing.

3. The trachea (windpipe) stays patent even when the neck is bent, because it consists of C-shaped arcs of cartilage joined by fibrous tissue and muscle, and lined by mucous membrane. It branches at the carina into right and left main bronchi.

4. The right main bronchus is wider and more vertical than the left. Inhaled foreign bodies, such as extracted teeth or peanuts, are therefore more likely to lodge on the right side.

The bronchial tree divides again and again into smaller and smaller branches, which eventually lead into the alveolar ducts.

Vocal cords

2. Besides acting as an air passage, the larynx closes to stop food entering the trachea during swallowing. Also, air passing over the vocal cords within it produces the voice. The epiglottis can swell during respiratory infections; this may block the airway, especially in a baby.

Pleural cavity

The trachea and bronchi are lined by respiratory epithelium, containing both mucus-secreting and ciliated cells. The cilia beat upwards moving an ascending escalator of sticky mucus, on which debris collects and is removed.

5. The alveoli are lined by a flat epithelium and are surrounded by the pulmonary capillaries. The barrier between the gas in the alveoli and the blood in the vessels is very thin, so oxygen and carbon dioxide can pass across it.

6 and 7. The lungs are able to expand because the inner (visceral) layer of pleura enclosing them is lubricated by pleural fluid and can slide on the outer layer of pleura lining the chest wall. In healthy people the pleural cavity is only a potential space.

How the respiratory system works

Components: 1. Movement of air in and out of the lungs; this is ventilation, comprising (a) inspiration (b) expiration
2. Free passage of air down the airway; that is airways function 3. Gas exchange 4. Control of respiration

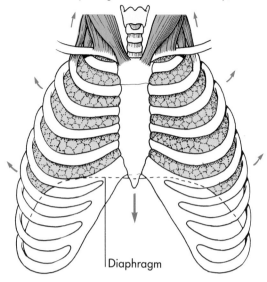

Diaphragm

1. Ventilation

(a) Inspiration (breathing in) happens because the chest cavity gets bigger, so the lungs expand and air is sucked into them. Contraction of the intercostal muscles raises the upper ribs like bucket handles on their joints to the sternum and spine. This widens the chest from side to side and makes it slightly deeper from front to back. As the diaphragm contracts its dome flattens, increasing the height of the chest from top to bottom. Once it has descended far enough to be fixed against the abdominal viscera, the diaphragm contracts further to raise the lower ribs and make the chest cavity even wider. When very deep breaths are taken, the scalene and sternomastoid muscles in the neck raise the whole rib cage, increasing all diameters of the chest cavity and allowing the diaphragm a wider range of movement.

(b) Expiration (breathing out) is passive in healthy people. The respiratory muscles gradually relax and the elastic lungs, bronchial tree and chest wall recoil to their original position. (A balloon is inflated actively but deflates alone, in the same way.)

Inspiration is less efficient if:
— pain limits chest wall movements, as in a patient with fractured ribs. Pneumonia may develop in the underinflated lung
— descent of the diaphragm is restricted by pregnancy, abdominal masses or simply the weight and bulk of the abdominal contents in a patient lying flat
— fluid (pleural effusion) or air (pneumothorax) in the pleural cavity prevents the lung from expanding fully.

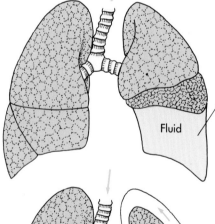

Fluid

Pleural effusion can be caused by:
— infection
— malignancy — secondary deposits in pleura
— low protein states such as cirrhosis or nephrotic syndrome
— heart failure
— pulmonary infarction (death of lung tissue).

Aspiration by needle is useful for:
— diagnosis: the concentration of protein or the presence of cells or bacteria can indicate the cause. A pleural biopsy may also be useful.
— treatment, relieving breathlessness. The cause should also be treated where possible, or the effusion may recur.

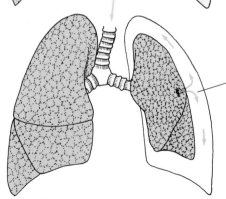

Pneumothorax can be:
— spontaneous, from rupture of a lung 'bleb' just beneath the pleura. Small amounts of air, occupying less than 20% of the hemithorax, can be left to absorb naturally; larger ones may be drained through an intercostal tube. Recurrent episodes may need surgical treatment.
— secondary to lung disease, such as emphysema, when a bulla leaks air.
— traumatic, eg following road accidents or cardiac massage.

SYSTEMS OF LIFE

Expiration is less efficient when the lung's elastic tissue has lost some of its spring because of ageing changes or disease such as emphysema. People with emphysema often also have chronic bronchitis, with a chronic cough producing sputum.

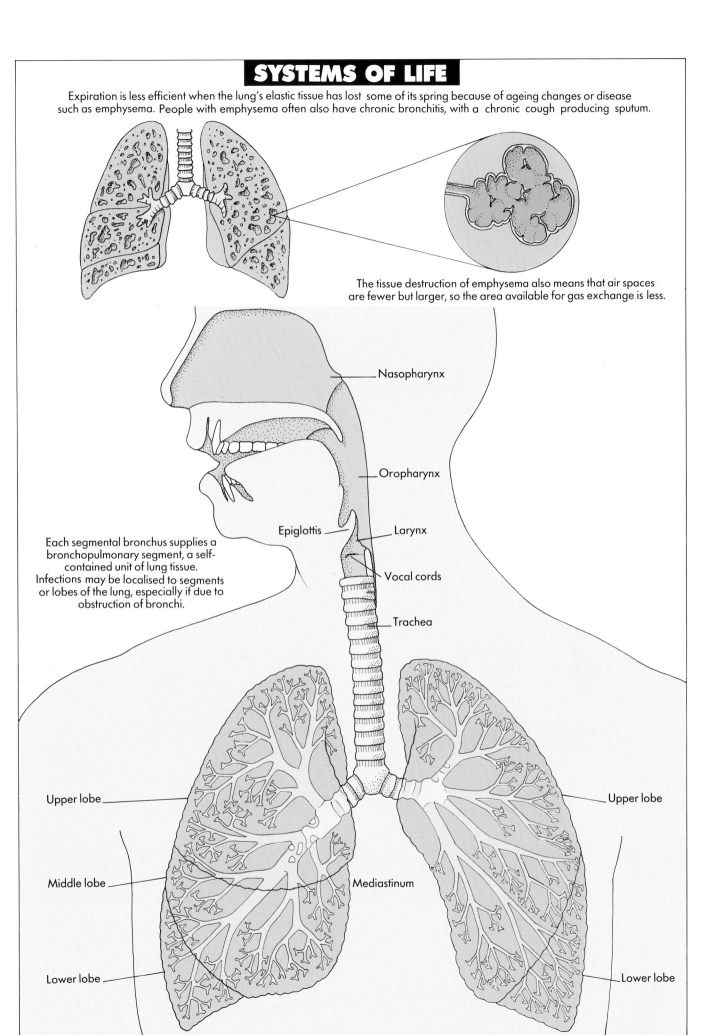

The tissue destruction of emphysema also means that air spaces are fewer but larger, so the area available for gas exchange is less.

Nasopharynx

Oropharynx

Epiglottis

Larynx

Vocal cords

Each segmental bronchus supplies a bronchopulmonary segment, a self-contained unit of lung tissue. Infections may be localised to segments or lobes of the lung, especially if due to obstruction of bronchi.

Trachea

Upper lobe

Upper lobe

Middle lobe

Mediastinum

Lower lobe

Lower lobe

If an unconscious patient aspirates fluid (eg vomit, blood), it will run into whichever part of the lung is the lowest (most dependent). There it will set up an aspiration pneumonia.

For example,
with the patient lying on his back:
apical segment
of right lower lobe;

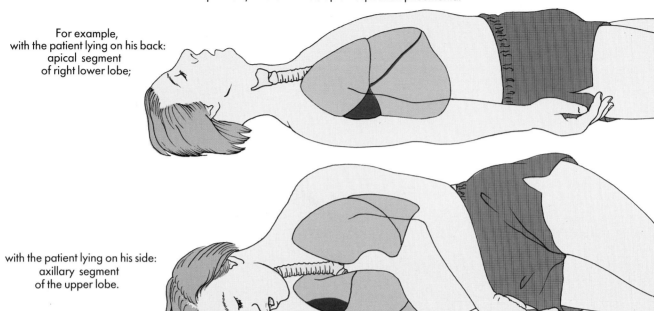

with the patient lying on his side:
axillary segment
of the upper lobe.

2. Airways function

A clear airway from nose or mouth to the depths of the lungs is essential to life. It can be blocked by:
— obstruction of the lumen of the tube by food, vomit, false teeth or the flaccid tongue of an unconscious patient (pharynx), inhaled peanuts or teeth (bronchi) or secretions (small bronchi and alveolar ducts)
— contraction of the muscle wall (bronchospasm) or thickening of the lining, for instance, by a bronchial carcinoma ('lung cancer')
— pressure from outside, for instance, by a lymph node enlarged by tuberculosis or cancer. When the large airways (larynx or trachea) are partially blocked, inspiration is prolonged, as in croup or mediastinal compression. When the small airways are narrowed, such as the bronchi in asthma, expiration is prolonged. This happens because:
— the lining mucosa swells
— the muscle of the wall contracts (bronchospasm)
— mucus blocks the lumen.

A patient with a lump of food blocking his larynx can neither speak nor breathe. He turns pale, becomes cyanosed and, if the block is not cleared, collapses and dies. The Heimlich manoeuvre can be used.

The Heimlich manoeuvre forces the diaphragm rapidly upwards, producing a violent upward gush of air which dislodges the food mass from the larynx.

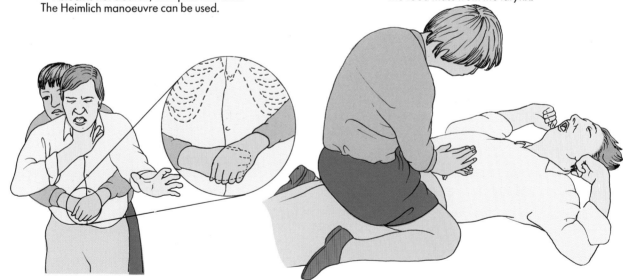

With a standing victim, the helper stands behind him, encircles the victim's waist with her arms and puts her right fist, thumb innermost, in the epigastrium pointing upwards. The helper then covers her fist with her left hand and pulls inwards and upwards into the victim's epigastrium, repeating the procedure if necessary.

With a recumbent victim, the helper sits astride the victim's hips and applies pressure to the victim's epigastrium as shown in the above picture.

SYSTEMS OF LIFE
The respiratory system Part II

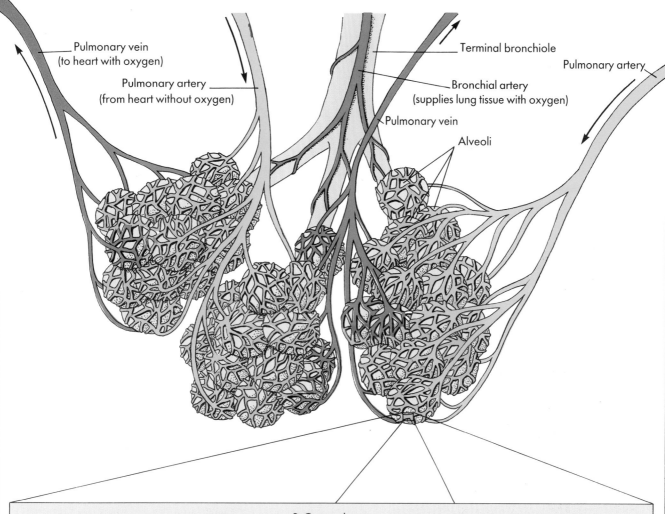

Pulmonary vein
(to heart with oxygen)

Pulmonary artery
(from heart without oxygen)

Terminal bronchiole

Pulmonary artery

Bronchial artery
(supplies lung tissue with oxygen)

Pulmonary vein

Alveoli

3. Gas exchange

In the depths of the lungs, oxygen from the inspired air in the alveolus passes across the alveolar membrane and the capillary wall to combine with the red oxygen-carrying pigment haemoglobin in the red blood cells. Simultaneously, carbon dioxide diffuses back from plasma and blood into the alveolar air so it can be breathed out with the next breath.

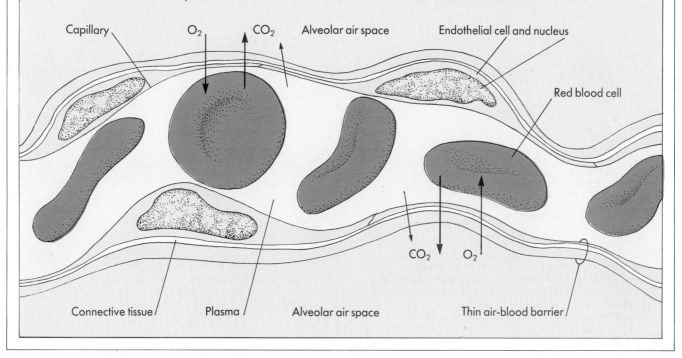

Capillary

O_2

CO_2

Alveolar air space

Endothelial cell and nucleus

Red blood cell

CO_2

O_2

Connective tissue

Plasma

Alveolar air space

Thin air-blood barrier

Gas exchange is less efficient if:

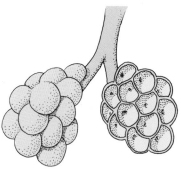

Normal alveoli

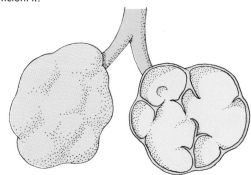

Emphysema

— the barrier is thickened by the growth of interstitial connective tissue, as in diseases like pulmonary fibrosis, silicosis and asbestosis.
— there are fewer alveoli than normal because lung tissue has been surgically removed or destroyed by a disease such as emphysema.

Embolus

— some alveoli are ventilated by air but not perfused by blood, as when a blood vessel is blocked by a pulmonary embolus.

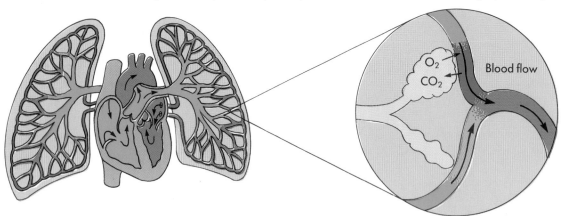

O_2
CO_2
Blood flow

— some alveoli are perfused by blood but not ventilated by air, as when part of the lung is collapsed or severely infected.
— there are fewer haemoglobin-rich red cells available to pick up oxygen, as in anaemia.

Blood gas determinations

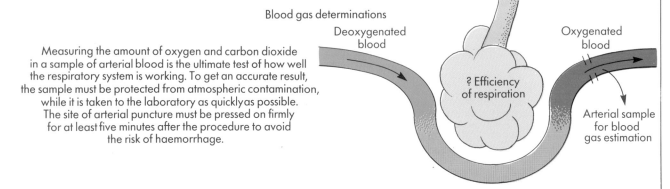

Deoxygenated blood

Oxygenated blood

Measuring the amount of oxygen and carbon dioxide in a sample of arterial blood is the ultimate test of how well the respiratory system is working. To get an accurate result, the sample must be protected from atmospheric contamination, while it is taken to the laboratory as quickly as possible. The site of arterial puncture must be pressed on firmly for at least five minutes after the procedure to avoid the risk of haemorrhage.

? Efficiency of respiration

Arterial sample for blood gas estimation

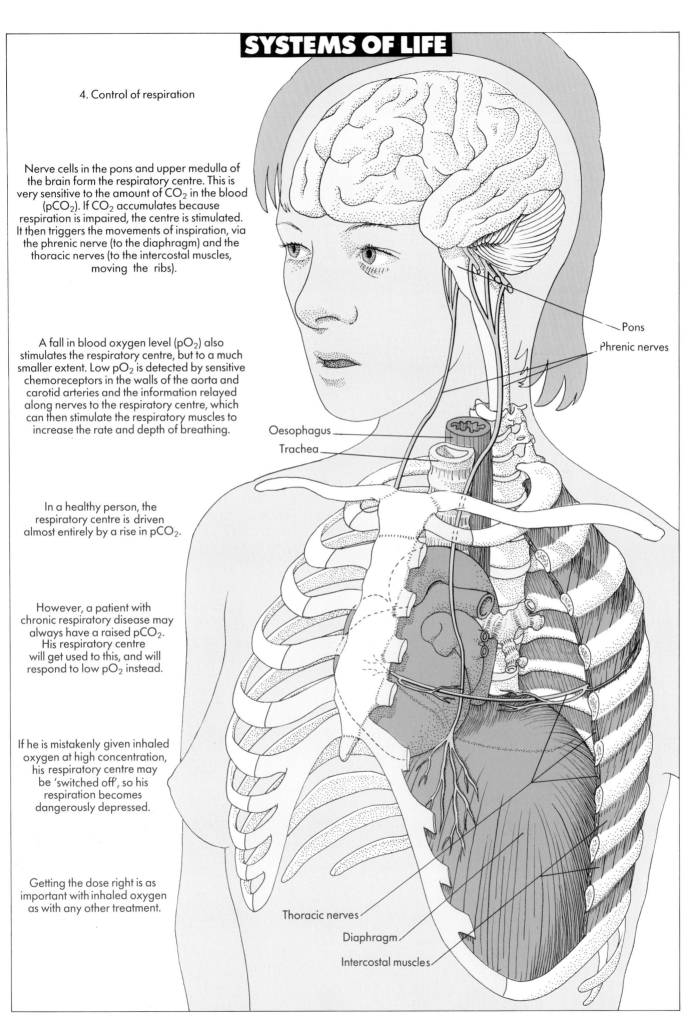

SYSTEMS OF LIFE

4. Control of respiration

Nerve cells in the pons and upper medulla of the brain form the respiratory centre. This is very sensitive to the amount of CO_2 in the blood (pCO_2). If CO_2 accumulates because respiration is impaired, the centre is stimulated. It then triggers the movements of inspiration, via the phrenic nerve (to the diaphragm) and the thoracic nerves (to the intercostal muscles, moving the ribs).

A fall in blood oxygen level (pO_2) also stimulates the respiratory centre, but to a much smaller extent. Low pO_2 is detected by sensitive chemoreceptors in the walls of the aorta and carotid arteries and the information relayed along nerves to the respiratory centre, which can then stimulate the respiratory muscles to increase the rate and depth of breathing.

In a healthy person, the respiratory centre is driven almost entirely by a rise in pCO_2.

However, a patient with chronic respiratory disease may always have a raised pCO_2. His respiratory centre will get used to this, and will respond to low pO_2 instead.

If he is mistakenly given inhaled oxygen at high concentration, his respiratory centre may be 'switched off', so his respiration becomes dangerously depressed.

Getting the dose right is as important with inhaled oxygen as with any other treatment.

Pons

Phrenic nerves

Oesophagus

Trachea

Thoracic nerves

Diaphragm

Intercostal muscles

SYSTEMS OF LIFE

Nursing observations of the respiratory system
Respiration becomes unnatural whenever it is thought about. Good observations can only be made when the patient is unaware of them.

Respiratory rate is very variable, with a range of about 12–20 breaths/minute in adults; babies and young children breathe faster. In a healthy person there is one breath to about every four pulse beats.

Tachypnoea (fast breathing) occurs:
— with exertion
— in emotional excitement
— in feverish illnesses; it is an especially important sign of pneumonia in elderly people
— to compensate for shallow respiration by shifting more air. This happens when respiratory movements are limited; for example, by the pain of pleurisy.

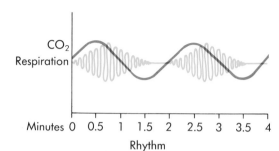

Rhythm
A particular sort of irregular breathing, Cheyne-Stokes respiration, is seen in some patients with:
— raised intracranial pressure; for instance, after a head injury or stroke
— narcotic overdose
— cardiac or renal failure.

Cyanosis
This is a bluish colour of the skin and mucous membranes which is noticeable when more than 5g haemoglobin/dl of blood is in the reduced form, deoxyhaemoglobin, which does not contain oxygen. This can be noticed in some patients with poor respiration, and is a sign of low arterial pO_2.

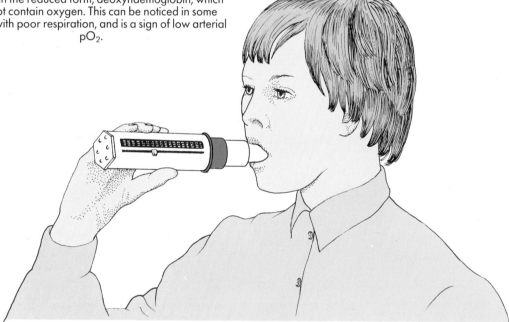

Peak flow
This can be measured with a peak flow meter. It records the maximum rate at which air can be breathed out when the patient has taken a big breath and expels it as hard and as fast as possible. The normal rate is 400–600 litres/minute. Serial readings can be a useful measure of the progress of a disease such as asthma.

Effect of poor respiratory function on daily living activities

Communication may be affected in several ways

Mobility, work, sexual expression and self-care may all be limited by breathlessness on exertion.

Laryngectomy (removal of the larynx, usually because of cancer) abolishes the normal power of speech. However, some patients learn oesophageal speech.

Sleeping may be more comfortable propped in a semi-sitting position. This helps the diaphragm to move freely by shifting the abdominal contents away from it.

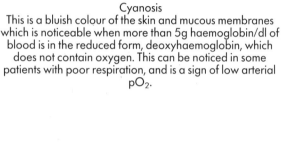

Artificial voice box can sometimes be made

Breathlessness may also interfere with talking. An asthmatic patient who cannot carry on a normal conversation requires urgent treatment.

SYSTEMS OF LIFE
The digestive system Part I

The purpose of the digestive system is to break down and absorb food.
Energy can then be liberated from it, and food constituents used for body repair and growth.
Waste and debris are then passed out.

The digestive system consists of:

— the alimentary canal (gut), a muscular tube about 9 metres (30ft) long, running from mouth to anus
— its accessory organs: the teeth, salivary glands, liver and biliary system and pancreas.

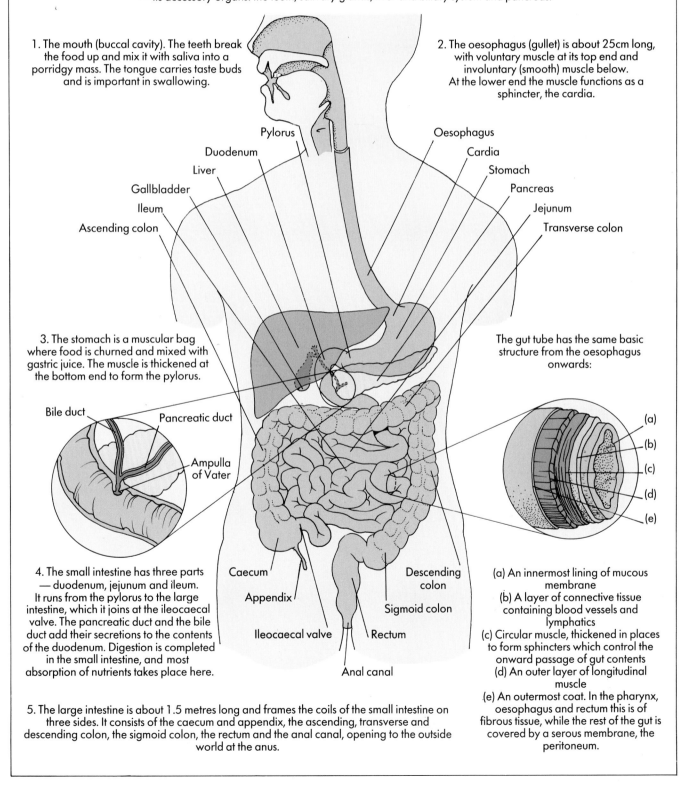

1. The mouth (buccal cavity). The teeth break the food up and mix it with saliva into a porridgy mass. The tongue carries taste buds and is important in swallowing.

2. The oesophagus (gullet) is about 25cm long, with voluntary muscle at its top end and involuntary (smooth) muscle below. At the lower end the muscle functions as a sphincter, the cardia.

Pylorus
Duodenum
Liver
Gallbladder
Ileum
Ascending colon

Oesophagus
Cardia
Stomach
Pancreas
Jejunum
Transverse colon

3. The stomach is a muscular bag where food is churned and mixed with gastric juice. The muscle is thickened at the bottom end to form the pylorus.

The gut tube has the same basic structure from the oesophagus onwards:

Bile duct
Pancreatic duct
Ampulla of Vater

(a)
(b)
(c)
(d)
(e)

4. The small intestine has three parts — duodenum, jejunum and ileum. It runs from the pylorus to the large intestine, which it joins at the ileocaecal valve. The pancreatic duct and the bile duct add their secretions to the contents of the duodenum. Digestion is completed in the small intestine, and most absorption of nutrients takes place here.

Caecum
Appendix
Ileocaecal valve

Descending colon
Sigmoid colon
Rectum

Anal canal

(a) An innermost lining of mucous membrane
(b) A layer of connective tissue containing blood vessels and lymphatics
(c) Circular muscle, thickened in places to form sphincters which control the onward passage of gut contents
(d) An outer layer of longitudinal muscle
(e) An outermost coat. In the pharynx, oesophagus and rectum this is of fibrous tissue, while the rest of the gut is covered by a serous membrane, the peritoneum.

5. The large intestine is about 1.5 metres long and frames the coils of the small intestine on three sides. It consists of the caecum and appendix, the ascending, transverse and descending colon, the sigmoid colon, the rectum and the anal canal, opening to the outside world at the anus.

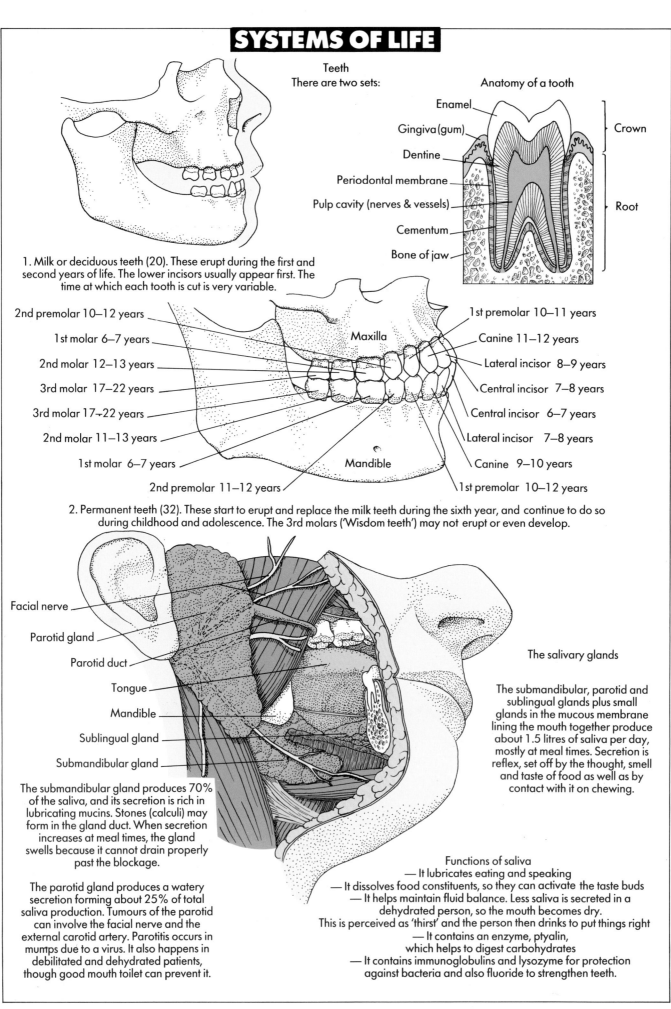

Teeth
There are two sets:

Anatomy of a tooth

- Enamel
- Gingiva (gum)
- Dentine
- Periodontal membrane
- Pulp cavity (nerves & vessels)
- Cementum
- Bone of jaw

Crown

Root

1. Milk or deciduous teeth (20). These erupt during the first and second years of life. The lower incisors usually appear first. The time at which each tooth is cut is very variable.

2nd premolar 10–12 years
1st molar 6–7 years
2nd molar 12–13 years
3rd molar 17–22 years
3rd molar 17–22 years
2nd molar 11–13 years
1st molar 6–7 years
2nd premolar 11–12 years

Maxilla

Mandible

1st premolar 10–11 years
Canine 11–12 years
Lateral incisor 8–9 years
Central incisor 7–8 years
Central incisor 6–7 years
Lateral incisor 7–8 years
Canine 9–10 years
1st premolar 10–12 years

2. Permanent teeth (32). These start to erupt and replace the milk teeth during the sixth year, and continue to do so during childhood and adolescence. The 3rd molars ('Wisdom teeth') may not erupt or even develop.

- Facial nerve
- Parotid gland
- Parotid duct
- Tongue
- Mandible
- Sublingual gland
- Submandibular gland

The salivary glands

The submandibular, parotid and sublingual glands plus small glands in the mucous membrane lining the mouth together produce about 1.5 litres of saliva per day, mostly at meal times. Secretion is reflex, set off by the thought, smell and taste of food as well as by contact with it on chewing.

The submandibular gland produces 70% of the saliva, and its secretion is rich in lubricating mucins. Stones (calculi) may form in the gland duct. When secretion increases at meal times, the gland swells because it cannot drain properly past the blockage.

The parotid gland produces a watery secretion forming about 25% of total saliva production. Tumours of the parotid can involve the facial nerve and the external carotid artery. Parotitis occurs in mumps due to a virus. It also happens in debilitated and dehydrated patients, though good mouth toilet can prevent it.

Functions of saliva
— It lubricates eating and speaking
— It dissolves food constituents, so they can activate the taste buds
— It helps maintain fluid balance. Less saliva is secreted in a dehydrated person, so the mouth becomes dry.
This is perceived as 'thirst' and the person then drinks to put things right
— It contains an enzyme, ptyalin, which helps to digest carbohydrates
— It contains immunoglobulins and lysozyme for protection against bacteria and also fluoride to strengthen teeth.

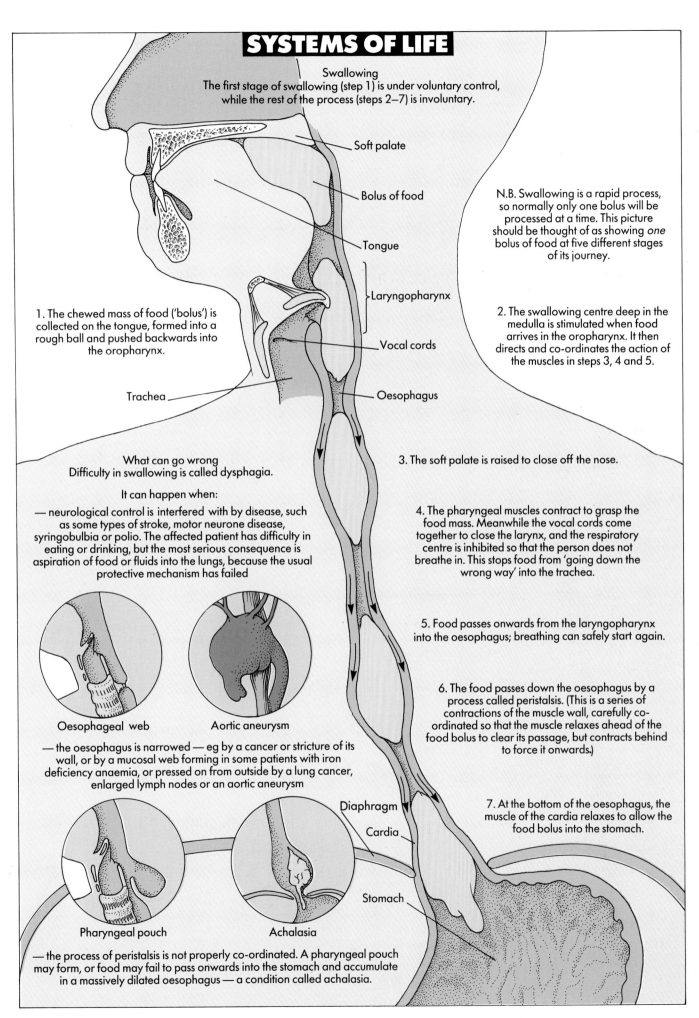

Swallowing
The first stage of swallowing (step 1) is under voluntary control, while the rest of the process (steps 2–7) is involuntary.

Soft palate

Bolus of food

Tongue

Laryngopharynx

Vocal cords

Oesophagus

Trachea

N.B. Swallowing is a rapid process, so normally only one bolus will be processed at a time. This picture should be thought of as showing *one* bolus of food at five different stages of its journey.

1. The chewed mass of food ('bolus') is collected on the tongue, formed into a rough ball and pushed backwards into the oropharynx.

2. The swallowing centre deep in the medulla is stimulated when food arrives in the oropharynx. It then directs and co-ordinates the action of the muscles in steps 3, 4 and 5.

What can go wrong
Difficulty in swallowing is called dysphagia.

It can happen when:

— neurological control is interfered with by disease, such as some types of stroke, motor neurone disease, syringobulbia or polio. The affected patient has difficulty in eating or drinking, but the most serious consequence is aspiration of food or fluids into the lungs, because the usual protective mechanism has failed

3. The soft palate is raised to close off the nose.

4. The pharyngeal muscles contract to grasp the food mass. Meanwhile the vocal cords come together to close the larynx, and the respiratory centre is inhibited so that the person does not breathe in. This stops food from 'going down the wrong way' into the trachea.

5. Food passes onwards from the laryngopharynx into the oesophagus; breathing can safely start again.

Oesophageal web

Aortic aneurysm

— the oesophagus is narrowed — eg by a cancer or stricture of its wall, or by a mucosal web forming in some patients with iron deficiency anaemia, or pressed on from outside by a lung cancer, enlarged lymph nodes or an aortic aneurysm

6. The food passes down the oesophagus by a process called peristalsis. (This is a series of contractions of the muscle wall, carefully co-ordinated so that the muscle relaxes ahead of the food bolus to clear its passage, but contracts behind to force it onwards.)

Diaphragm

Cardia

7. At the bottom of the oesophagus, the muscle of the cardia relaxes to allow the food bolus into the stomach.

Stomach

Pharyngeal pouch

Achalasia

— the process of peristalsis is not properly co-ordinated. A pharyngeal pouch may form, or food may fail to pass onwards into the stomach and accumulate in a massively dilated oesophagus — a condition called achalasia.

Vomiting
The vomiting centre in the medulla can respond to many different sorts of stimuli:

— distension of the stomach by overeating, or gastric irritation by poisons or alcohol
— hormonal changes of pregnancy
— some medicines, eg morphine and its derivatives
— irradiation, either accidental or when used in radiotherapy

— raised intracranial pressure, eg from a brain tumour
— unaccustomed movement, which disturbs the balance mechanism of the inner ear (motion sickness)
— the gag reflex, produced by touching the back of the pharynx
— mental distress from severe pain or unpleasant sights, smells or ideas.

Signs of impending vomiting include: nausea, increased secretion of saliva, a fast heart rate, pallor, sweating and dilation of the pupils.

How it happens

1. The patient pauses between breaths, his diaphragm becomes fixed and his vocal cords close to protect the respiratory tree.

2. The abdominal wall muscles contract, increasing the pressure inside the abdomen.

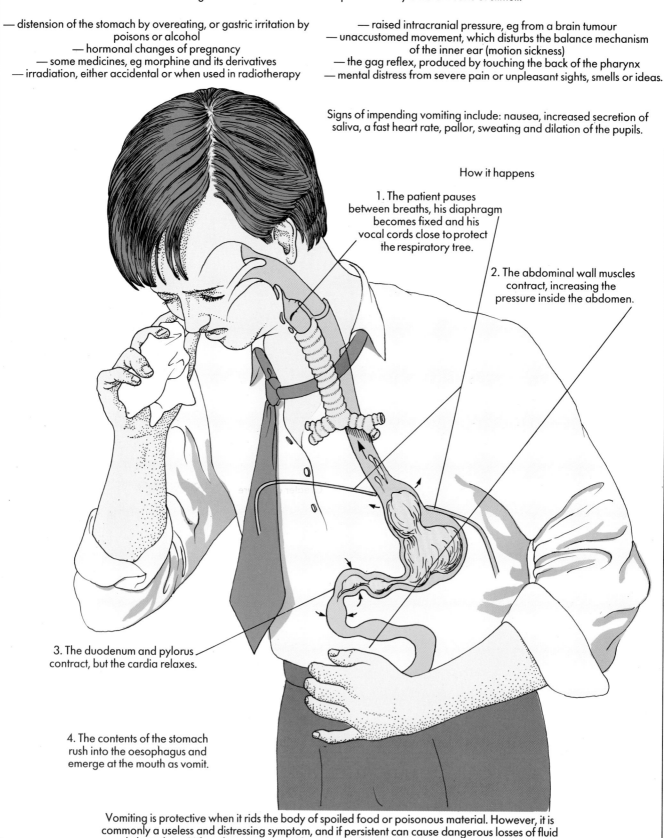

3. The duodenum and pylorus contract, but the cardia relaxes.

4. The contents of the stomach rush into the oesophagus and emerge at the mouth as vomit.

Vomiting is protective when it rids the body of spoiled food or poisonous material. However, it is commonly a useless and distressing symptom, and if persistent can cause dangerous losses of fluid and electrolytes. When the cause cannot be removed, antiemetic drugs may be prescribed, eg hyoscine and the antihistamines. These suppress the action of the vomiting centre, but may also cause unwanted effects of drowsiness, blurred vision, dry mouth and retention of urine.

SYSTEMS OF LIFE
The digestive system Part II

Digestion has two parts:

1. A mechanical process, in which food constituents are mashed into smaller particles and mixed with digestive juices.

2. A chemical process, in which the enzymes in the juices break down food substances so that their molecules become small and simple enough to be absorbed into the body. An enzyme is named according to the substance it digests — eg lipase breaks down lipids, peptidase breaks down peptides, and so on.

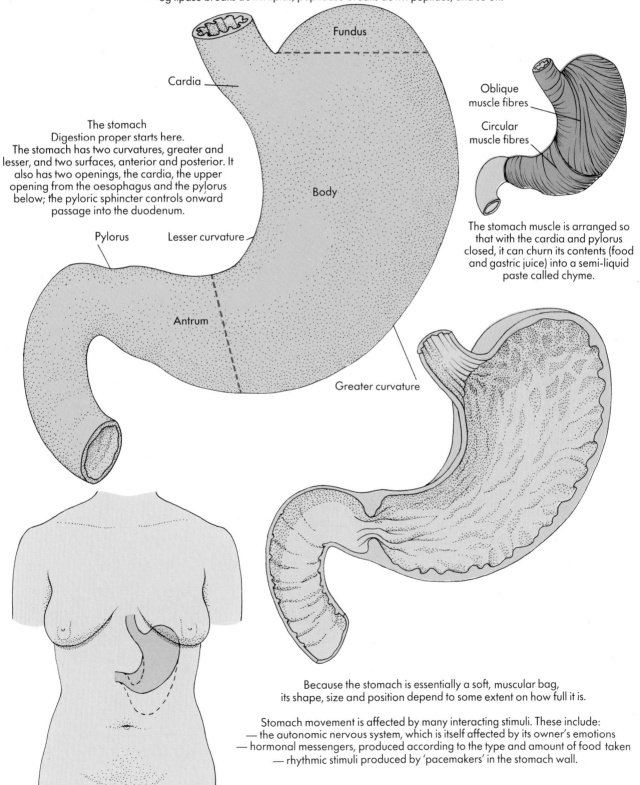

Fundus

Cardia

Oblique muscle fibres

Circular muscle fibres

The stomach
Digestion proper starts here.
The stomach has two curvatures, greater and lesser, and two surfaces, anterior and posterior. It also has two openings, the cardia, the upper opening from the oesophagus and the pylorus below; the pyloric sphincter controls onward passage into the duodenum.

Body

The stomach muscle is arranged so that with the cardia and pylorus closed, it can churn its contents (food and gastric juice) into a semi-liquid paste called chyme.

Pylorus

Lesser curvature

Antrum

Greater curvature

Because the stomach is essentially a soft, muscular bag, its shape, size and position depend to some extent on how full it is.

Stomach movement is affected by many interacting stimuli. These include:
— the autonomic nervous system, which is itself affected by its owner's emotions
— hormonal messengers, produced according to the type and amount of food taken
— rhythmic stimuli produced by 'pacemakers' in the stomach wall.

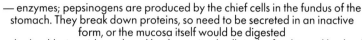

Meanwhile, gastric juice constituents produce chemical digestion.
The stomach's lining mucosa secretes:

— enzymes; pepsinogens are produced by the chief cells in the fundus of the
stomach. They break down proteins, so need to be secreted in an inactive
form, or the mucosa itself would be digested
— hydrochloric acid, produced by the parietal cells in the fundus and body of
the stomach. This converts pepsinogens to their active forms (pepsins) and also
helps to kill bacteria in food
— mucus; this forms a coating for the stomach wall which is acid and
pepsin-resistant
— intrinsic factor, which bonds with vitamin B_{12} from the diet
— gastrin, a hormone which helps to control gastric secretion.

Control of secretion
The different types are described separately, but in life they act together
and are tailored to respond to the amount and sort of food eaten.

1. *Nervous control* (sometimes called the psychic-neural or
cephalic phase). When the person sees, smells, tastes or even thinks
of food, or when his brain is low in sugar because of hunger, the
vagus nerve stimulates the parietal cells to produce acid and the
hormones of the gastric antrum to produce gastrin.

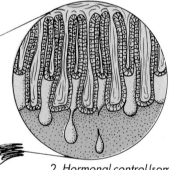

2. *Hormonal control* (sometimes called
the local or gastric phase). Food in the antrum
of the stomach releases the hormone gastrin.
This is carried in the blood to the upper part of
the stomach, where it stimulates acid production.
Less gastrin is produced when the stomach
contents are very acid — ie when there is
more than enough acid gastric juice for
the amount of food present.

3. *Intestinal phase*. Duodenal hormone secretion responds to gastric need. When large amounts of chyme stretch the duodenal wall
because a meal is being processed through the stomach, the hormones stimulate further production of gastric juice. However, as the
food passes onward, less chyme reaches the duodenum. Also, it becomes more acid, as more gastric juice is being produced than is
needed. When this happens, hormones are produced which switch off further secretion.

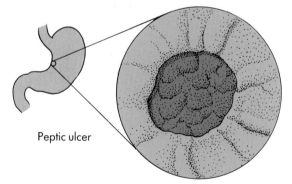

Peptic ulcer

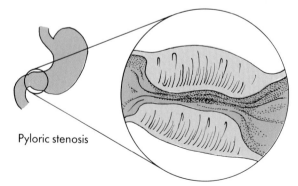

Pyloric stenosis

The acid-proof stomach lining and the careful regulation of acid
production help to stop the stomach from digesting either itself or
the adjacent duodenum. If the balance between acid and
protection breaks down, then peptic ulcers result.

In a healthy person, liquids leave the stomach through the
pylorus soon after entering it, while solids take 1–4 hours.
Emptying is delayed in patients with pyloric stenosis. This happens
in some babies with a hypertrophied pylorus and also in adults
with scarring from an old ulcer or a gastric cancer.

SYSTEMS OF LIFE

The small intestine
Digestion is completed in the small intestine, and almost all absorption of food takes place here.
The small intestine runs from the pylorus of the stomach to the ileocaecal valve, where it joins the large intestine.
Though usually described as being about 6 metres long, it may be much shorter in a living subject with good muscle tone.
It has three parts:

— the *duodenum*, about 25cm long, curving round the head of the pancreas. The pancreatic and bile ducts enter it at the ampulla of Vater

— the *jejunum*, 2 metres long. Its mucosa has folds to slow down the passage of food and increase its absorptive area

— the *ileum*, 3.5 — 4 metres long, opening into the large intestine at the caecum.

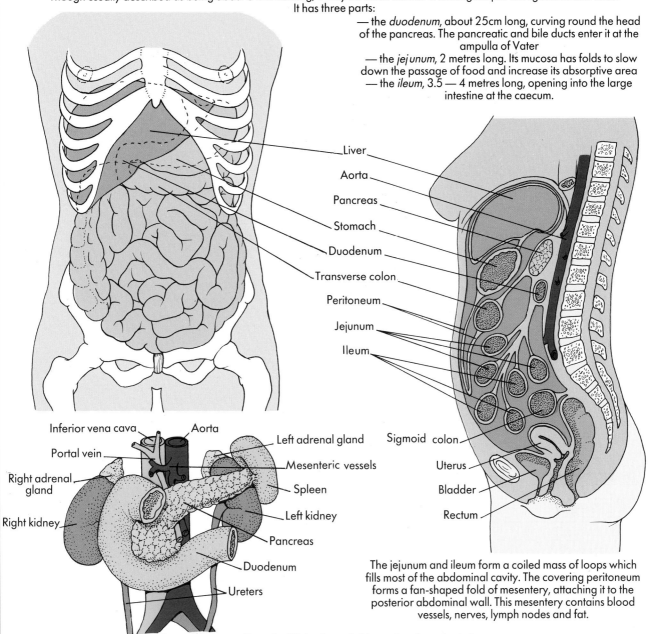

Liver
Aorta
Pancreas
Stomach
Duodenum
Transverse colon
Peritoneum
Jejunum
Ileum
Sigmoid colon
Uterus
Bladder
Rectum

Inferior vena cava
Aorta
Portal vein
Left adrenal gland
Mesenteric vessels
Right adrenal gland
Spleen
Left kidney
Right kidney
Pancreas
Duodenum
Ureters

The jejunum and ileum form a coiled mass of loops which fills most of the abdominal cavity. The covering peritoneum forms a fan-shaped fold of mesentery, attaching it to the posterior abdominal wall. This mesentery contains blood vessels, nerves, lymph nodes and fat.

A very big area of intestinal lining is available to absorb nutrients, because:

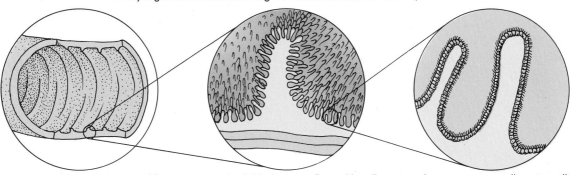

— the lining has folds, which are visible to the naked eye

— on the folds there are finger-like villi about 1mm long and 0.8mm in diameter. Because of these, the healthy mucosa looks like velvet

— there are even smaller microvilli on the surface of the villi.

The small intestine moves in three ways:

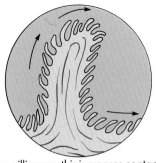

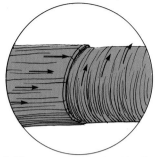

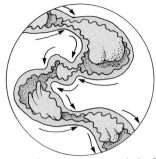

1. The villi wave; this increases contact between their absorptive surface and the food around them.

2. The contents are mixed by the action of longitudinal muscle and circular muscle.

3. Peristaltic movements push the food along the intestinal length.

Digestion in the small intestine happens because of:

— enzymes in the intestinal juice
— enzymes in pancreatic juice
— the action of bile produced by the liver; this contains no enzymes, but its bile salts emulsify fats so that water-soluble lipases can act on them.

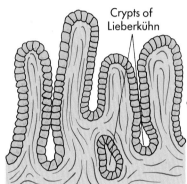

Crypts of Lieberkühn

Between the villi of the small intestine are the crypts of Lieberkühn. Cells here produce:
— digestive enzymes and anti-infective immunoglobulins
— the hormones secretin and cholecystokinin-pancreozymin (one substance, but with two actions and a name for each). These affect the production of bile and pancreatic juice, so they co-ordinate digestion here
— mucus, for protection and lubrication
— many new cells, to replace those scoured off the villi by passing food.

Bile secretion
About 700ml bile is produced each day. When it is not needed immediately (ie between meals), the sphincter of Oddi remains closed. The bile cannot enter the duodenum and it is diverted into the gall bladder. Here it is stored and concentrated by the removal of water.

Pancreatic secretion
The pancreas produces about 2 litres of juice per day which contains:
— bicarbonate, to neutralise remaining stomach acid in the food
— the enzyme precursors trypsinogen and chymotrypsinogen. These are activated to trypsin and chymotrypsin in the duodenum. This is necessary as they digest protein; if they become active in the pancreas, the gland digests itself
— the enzymes amylase, which splits starch into sugars, and lipase which acts on fats.

Right hepatic duct

Cystic duct

Left hepatic duct

Common hepatic duct

Common bile duct

Gall bladder

Bile

Pancreas

Duodenum

Pancreatic duct

Cholecystokinin-pancreozymin

Bicarbonate

Amylase

Lipase

Trypsinogen

Chymotrypsinogen

Bicarbonate
Amylase
Lipase
Trypsin
Chymotrypsin
Bile

Sphincter of Oddi

When bile is required to digest a fatty meal, the sphincter of Oddi relaxes and the gall bladder contracts, forcing its bile down the common bile duct into the duodenum. This happens partly as a nervous reflex and partly by the action of cholecystokinin-pancreozymin (CCK-PZ). As CCK-PZ is produced when there is fatty food in the duodenum, this ensures that bile is available when needed.

Chyme

Control of pancreatic secretion
This happens:
— partly by the vagus nerve
— partly by the duodenal hormones: secretin, whose production is stimulated by the presence of fat and acid chyme, and cholecystokinin-pancreozymin, stimulated by the presence of fat; this produces a juice that is very rich in enzymes.

Digestion and absorption of fat (simplified)

Fats ('lipids') are digested by enzymes called lipases. Most dietary fat is formed of triglycerides (TGs). Small amounts of TGs can be absorbed intact, but most are broken down to monoglycerides (MGs) and free fatty acids (FFAs). Lipids from oily foods need special treatment before they can mix with watery digestive juices. In the stomach, fat in food is emulsified into small droplets (1). When the stomach chyme passes on to the duodenum, pancreatic lipases can work on these droplets at the oil/water interface (2). The MGs and FFAs that result are acted on by bile salts and formed into micelles (3). These are packages whose fatty insides have a water-soluble covering which helps their absorption into intestinal cells (4). Once absorbed, they can be used for immediate energy or stored for later use (5).

BILE SALTS. These are made in the liver from cholesterol and flow into the duodenum in the bile. After use in fat absorption, they are absorbed in the ileum and carried back to the liver by the portal vein. This secretion and absorption process can happen several times during the digestion of a single fatty meal; it is sometimes called enterohepatic circulation.

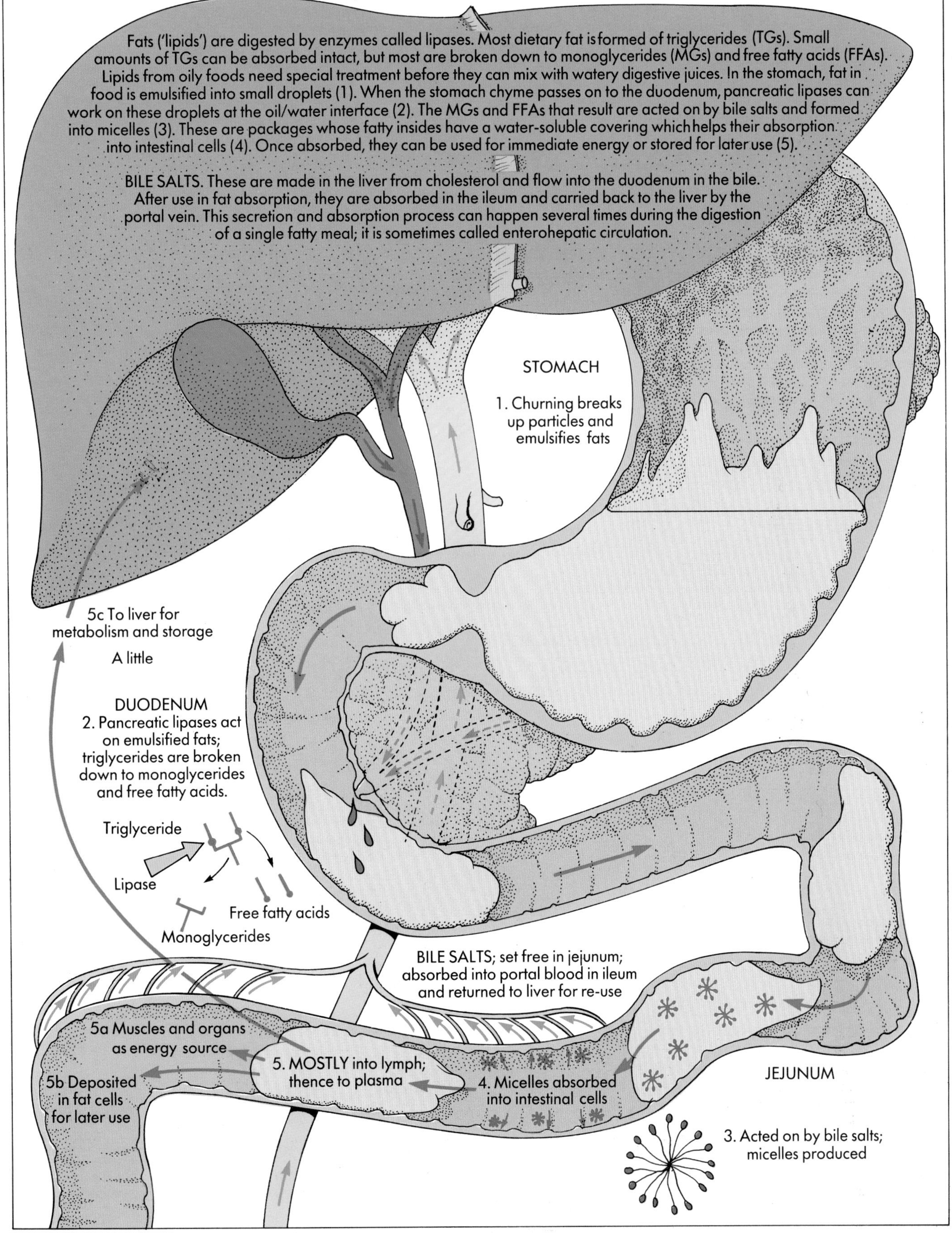

STOMACH

1. Churning breaks up particles and emulsifies fats

5c To liver for metabolism and storage

A little

DUODENUM
2. Pancreatic lipases act on emulsified fats; triglycerides are broken down to monoglycerides and free fatty acids.

Triglyceride

Lipase

Free fatty acids

Monoglycerides

BILE SALTS; set free in jejunum; absorbed into portal blood in ileum and returned to liver for re-use

5a Muscles and organs as energy source

5. MOSTLY into lymph; thence to plasma

4. Micelles absorbed into intestinal cells

JEJUNUM

5b Deposited in fat cells for later use

3. Acted on by bile salts; micelles produced

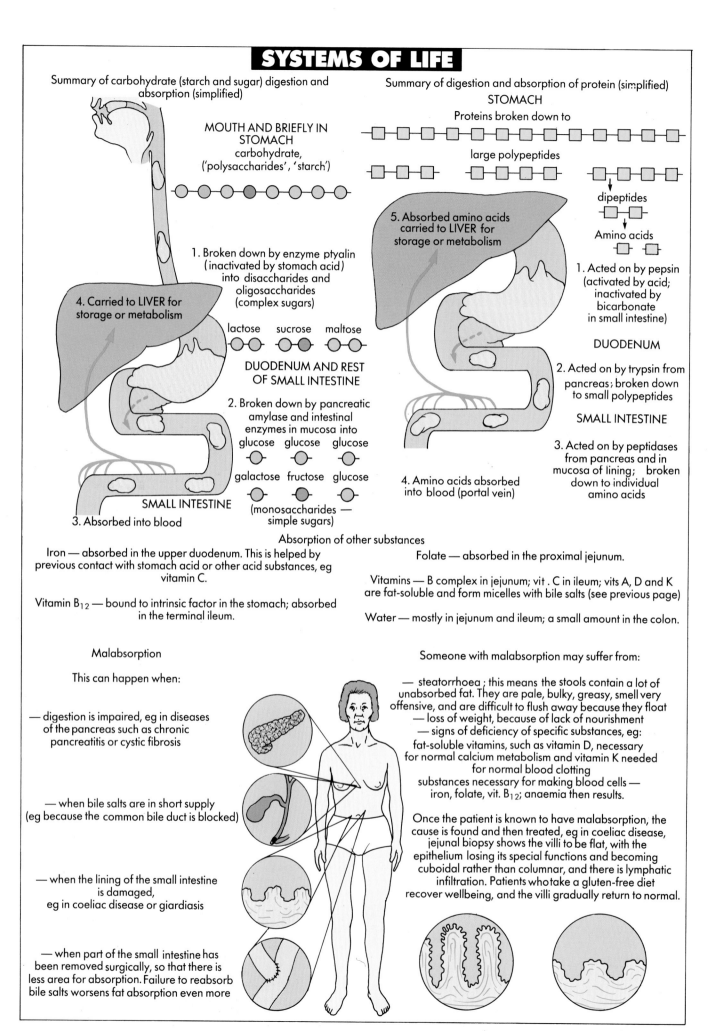

Summary of carbohydrate (starch and sugar) digestion and absorption (simplified)

MOUTH AND BRIEFLY IN STOMACH
carbohydrate, ('polysaccharides', 'starch')

4. Carried to LIVER for storage or metabolism

1. Broken down by enzyme ptyalin (inactivated by stomach acid) into disaccharides and oligosaccharides (complex sugars)

lactose   sucrose   maltose

DUODENUM AND REST OF SMALL INTESTINE

2. Broken down by pancreatic amylase and intestinal enzymes in mucosa into

glucose   glucose   glucose

galactose fructose   glucose

(monosaccharides — simple sugars)

SMALL INTESTINE
3. Absorbed into blood

Summary of digestion and absorption of protein (simplified)

STOMACH
Proteins broken down to

large polypeptides

dipeptides

Amino acids

5. Absorbed amino acids carried to LIVER for storage or metabolism

1. Acted on by pepsin (activated by acid; inactivated by bicarbonate in small intestine)

DUODENUM

2. Acted on by trypsin from pancreas; broken down to small polypeptides

SMALL INTESTINE

3. Acted on by peptidases from pancreas and in mucosa of lining; broken down to individual amino acids

4. Amino acids absorbed into blood (portal vein)

Absorption of other substances

Iron — absorbed in the upper duodenum. This is helped by previous contact with stomach acid or other acid substances, eg vitamin C.

Vitamin B_{12} — bound to intrinsic factor in the stomach; absorbed in the terminal ileum.

Folate — absorbed in the proximal jejunum.

Vitamins — B complex in jejunum; vit . C in ileum; vits A, D and K are fat-soluble and form micelles with bile salts (see previous page)

Water — mostly in jejunum and ileum; a small amount in the colon.

Malabsorption

This can happen when:

— digestion is impaired, eg in diseases of the pancreas such as chronic pancreatitis or cystic fibrosis

— when bile salts are in short supply (eg because the common bile duct is blocked)

— when the lining of the small intestine is damaged, eg in coeliac disease or giardiasis

— when part of the small intestine has been removed surgically, so that there is less area for absorption. Failure to reabsorb bile salts worsens fat absorption even more

Someone with malabsorption may suffer from:

— steatorrhoea ; this means the stools contain a lot of unabsorbed fat. They are pale, bulky, greasy, smell very offensive, and are difficult to flush away because they float
— loss of weight, because of lack of nourishment
— signs of deficiency of specific substances, eg:
fat-soluble vitamins, such as vitamin D, necessary for normal calcium metabolism and vitamin K needed for normal blood clotting
substances necessary for making blood cells — iron, folate, vit. B_{12}; anaemia then results.

Once the patient is known to have malabsorption, the cause is found and then treated, eg in coeliac disease, jejunal biopsy shows the villi to be flat, with the epithelium losing its special functions and becoming cuboidal rather than columnar, and there is lymphatic infiltration. Patients who take a gluten-free diet recover wellbeing, and the villi gradually return to normal.

SYSTEMS OF LIFE

The Liver

The liver is the largest gland in the body, weighing about 1.5kg. (The Greek word for liver is 'hepar'; hence 'hepatic — belonging to the liver'.) It is wedge-shaped, vascular and easily torn, lying mainly in the upper right part of the abdominal cavity. It has a large right and a smaller left lobe. The falciform ligament connects the liver to the underside of the diaphragm and to the anterior abdominal wall.

Functions of the liver

The liver is a very active organ, and manufactures, stores and breaks down substances in the body according to need. It is important in:

Manufacture: of plasma proteins and blood-clotting factors such as heparin, fibrinogen and prothrombin. Blood cells are made here in some diseases such as the leukaemias

Storage: of glycogen, which is broken down to glucose as needed; fat, iron, vitamins A and B_{12} and probably some proteins

Metabolism: of carbohydrate, fat and protein

Detoxification: of harmful substances taken by mouth and entering the body in other ways. Many medicines are metabolised by the liver, and its function may affect the desirable dose and route of administration

Secretion of bile: for digestion

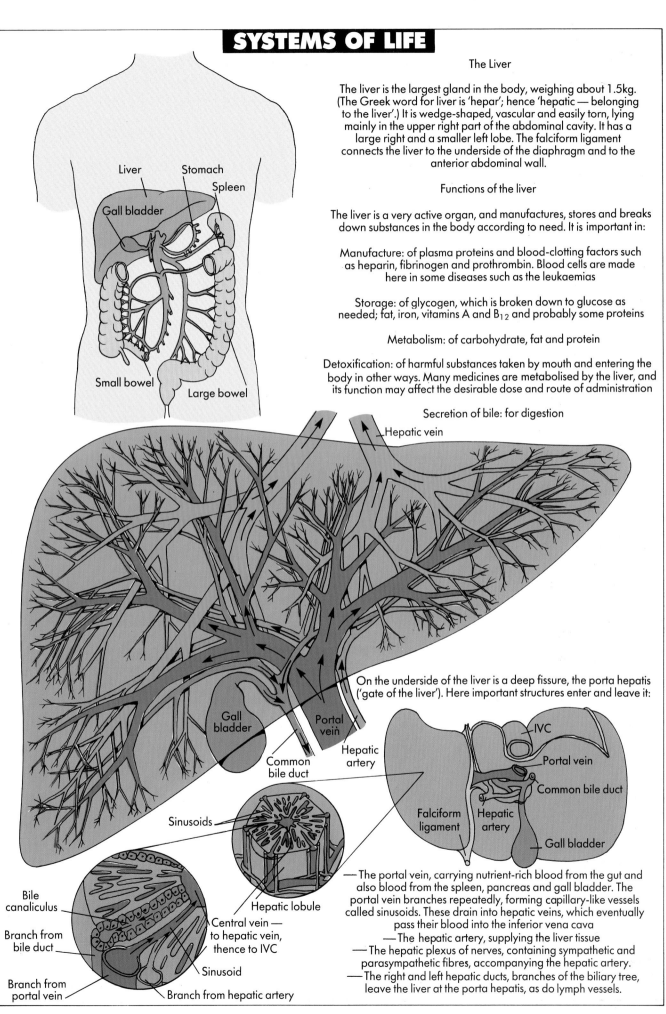

Liver
Stomach
Spleen
Gall bladder
Small bowel
Large bowel

Hepatic vein

Gall bladder
Portal vein
Common bile duct
Hepatic artery

On the underside of the liver is a deep fissure, the porta hepatis ('gate of the liver'). Here important structures enter and leave it:

IVC
Portal vein
Common bile duct
Falciform ligament
Hepatic artery
Gall bladder

Sinusoids
Hepatic lobule
Central vein — to hepatic vein, thence to IVC
Sinusoid
Bile canaliculus
Branch from bile duct
Branch from portal vein
Branch from hepatic artery

— The portal vein, carrying nutrient-rich blood from the gut and also blood from the spleen, pancreas and gall bladder. The portal vein branches repeatedly, forming capillary-like vessels called sinusoids. These drain into hepatic veins, which eventually pass their blood into the inferior vena cava
— The hepatic artery, supplying the liver tissue
— The hepatic plexus of nerves, containing sympathetic and parasympathetic fibres, accompanying the hepatic artery.
— The right and left hepatic ducts, branches of the biliary tree, leave the liver at the porta hepatis, as do lymph vessels.

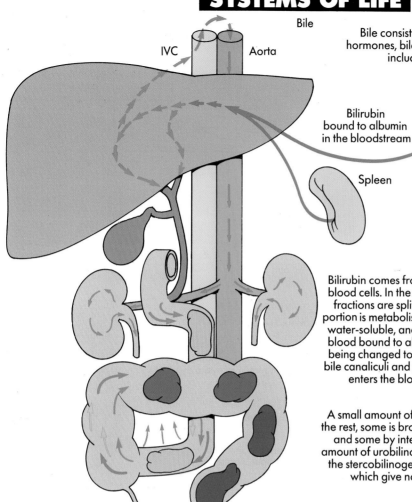

Bile

IVC   Aorta

Bile consists of water and electrolytes, bilirubin, steroid hormones, bile salts, cholesterol and many other substances, including some drugs excreted by the liver.

Bilirubin bound to albumin in the bloodstream

Spleen

Bilirubin

Bilirubin glucuronide

Urobilinogen

Stercobilinogen

Bilirubin comes from the breakdown of haemoglobin in old red blood cells. In the spleen and bone marrow the globin and iron fractions are split off from the molecule. The remaining haem portion is metabolised to bilirubin. This form is fat-soluble but not water-soluble, and so needs to be transported to the liver in the blood bound to albumin. In the liver it is made water-soluble by being changed to bilirubin glucuronide. This is secreted into the bile canaliculi and passes to the duodenum in the bile. Some also enters the bloodstream and is excreted by the kidneys.

A small amount of bilirubin is reabsorbed from the intestine. Of the rest, some is broken down in the liver and bile to urobilinogen and some by intestinal bacteria into stercobilinogen. A small amount of urobilinogen goes back to the liver, while the rest, with the stercobilinogen, is broken down in the bowel into products which give normal faeces (stools) their brown colour.

Jaundice

This happens when there is excess bilirubin in the plasma and tissue fluids. The skin and sclera (white of the eye) then become yellow. There are three types:

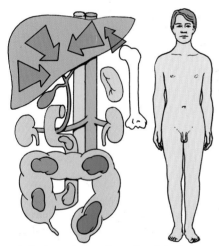

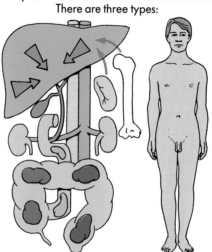

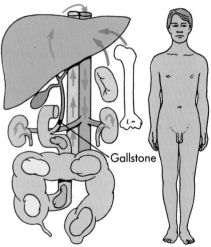

Gallstone

1. Prehepatic jaundice, when bilirubin production is increased. A common cause is haemolytic anaemia, with excess breakdown of red cells. If too much is produced for the available albumin to bind it safely on its way to the liver, the left-over fat-soluble bilirubin can produce brain damage. This is the mechanism of kernicterus, the type of cerebral palsy occurring in haemolytic disease of the newborn. Tests show increased fat-soluble bilirubin in blood; urine and stools are normal in colour.

2. Hepatic jaundice, when the liver cells are too damaged to process bilirubin properly (eg in hepatitis or cirrhosis), or when some of the necessary enzymes are congenitally absent. Tests will demonstrate the liver abnormality.

3. Post-hepatic jaundice, when free drainage of bile into the duodenum is blocked, eg by a gallstone in the common bile duct or by external pressure from a carcinoma of the head of the pancreas. Water-soluble bilirubin then appears in the blood, as does an excess of alkaline phosphatase, another substance normally excreted in the bile. The bilirubin gives the urine a dark colour, while the stools are pale because no bilirubin enters the intestine to be metabolised to brown pigments. These changes can be detected by laboratory tests.

SYSTEMS OF LIFE
The digestive system — Part 4

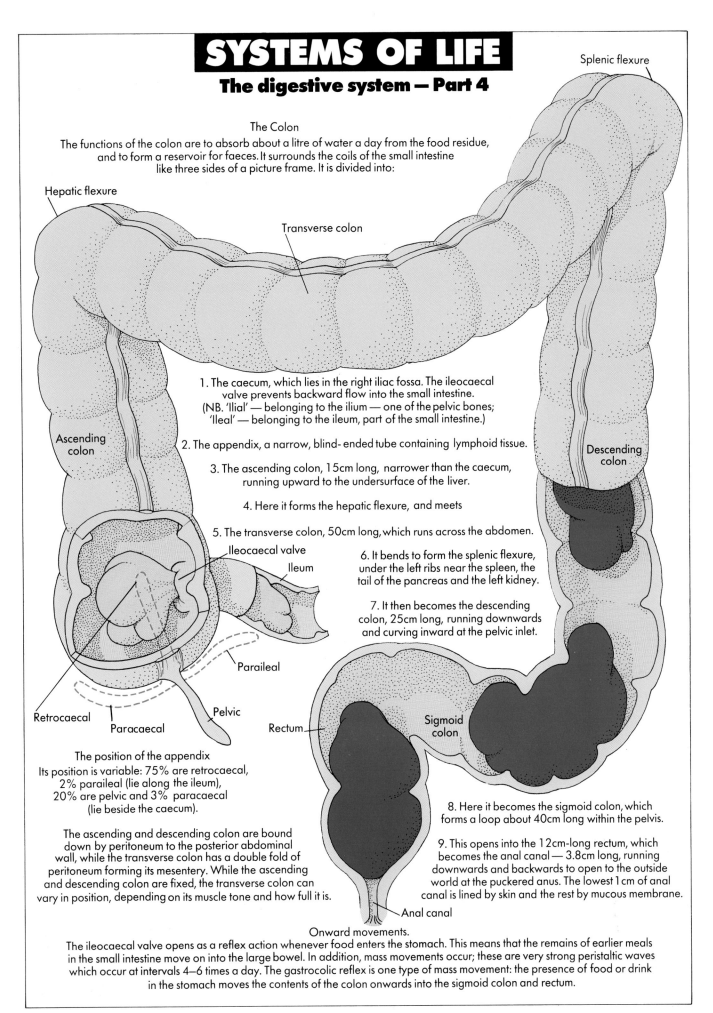

Splenic flexure

Hepatic flexure

The Colon
The functions of the colon are to absorb about a litre of water a day from the food residue, and to form a reservoir for faeces. It surrounds the coils of the small intestine like three sides of a picture frame. It is divided into:

Transverse colon

Ascending colon

Descending colon

1. The caecum, which lies in the right iliac fossa. The ileocaecal valve prevents backward flow into the small intestine.
(NB. 'Ilial' — belonging to the ilium — one of the pelvic bones; 'Ileal' — belonging to the ileum, part of the small intestine.)

2. The appendix, a narrow, blind- ended tube containing lymphoid tissue.

3. The ascending colon, 15cm long, narrower than the caecum, running upward to the undersurface of the liver.

4. Here it forms the hepatic flexure, and meets

5. The transverse colon, 50cm long, which runs across the abdomen.

Ileocaecal valve

Ileum

6. It bends to form the splenic flexure, under the left ribs near the spleen, the tail of the pancreas and the left kidney.

7. It then becomes the descending colon, 25cm long, running downwards and curving inward at the pelvic inlet.

Paraileal

Retrocaecal

Paracaecal

Pelvic

Rectum

Sigmoid colon

The position of the appendix
Its position is variable: 75% are retrocaecal, 2% paraileal (lie along the ileum), 20% are pelvic and 3% paracaecal (lie beside the caecum).

8. Here it becomes the sigmoid colon, which forms a loop about 40cm long within the pelvis.

The ascending and descending colon are bound down by peritoneum to the posterior abdominal wall, while the transverse colon has a double fold of peritoneum forming its mesentery. While the ascending and descending colon are fixed, the transverse colon can vary in position, depending on its muscle tone and how full it is.

9. This opens into the 12cm-long rectum, which becomes the anal canal — 3.8cm long, running downwards and backwards to open to the outside world at the puckered anus. The lowest 1cm of anal canal is lined by skin and the rest by mucous membrane.

Anal canal

Onward movements.
The ileocaecal valve opens as a reflex action whenever food enters the stomach. This means that the remains of earlier meals in the small intestine move on into the large bowel. In addition, mass movements occur; these are very strong peristaltic waves which occur at intervals 4–6 times a day. The gastrocolic reflex is one type of mass movement: the presence of food or drink in the stomach moves the contents of the colon onwards into the sigmoid colon and rectum.

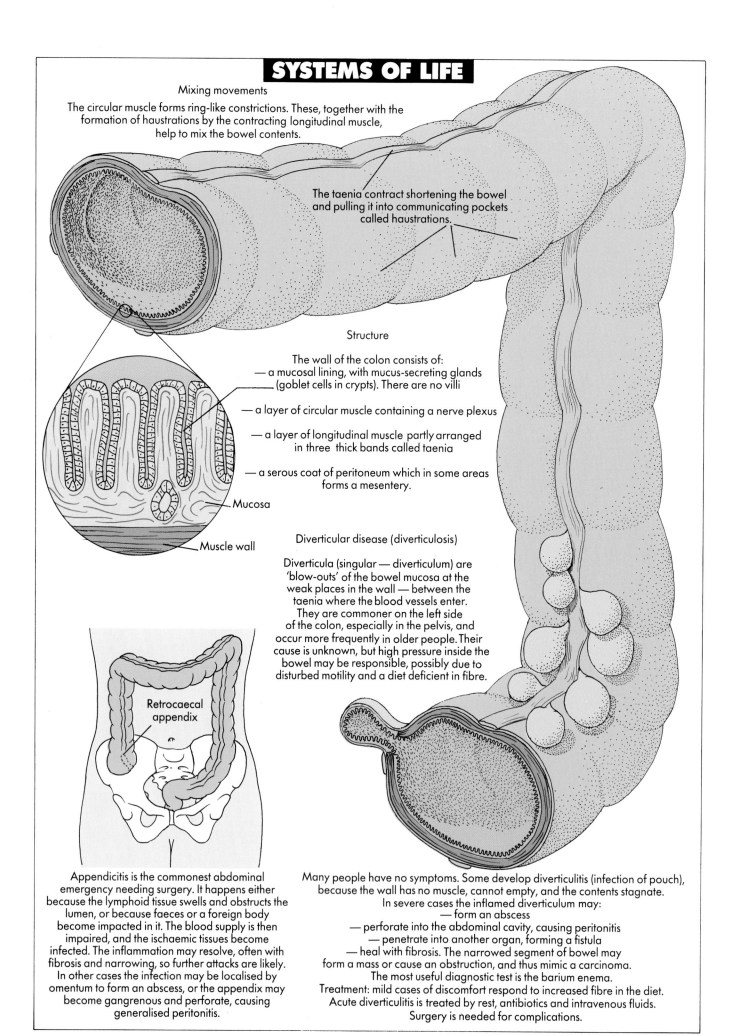

Mixing movements

The circular muscle forms ring-like constrictions. These, together with the formation of haustrations by the contracting longitudinal muscle, help to mix the bowel contents.

The taenia contract shortening the bowel and pulling it into communicating pockets called haustrations.

Structure

The wall of the colon consists of:
— a mucosal lining, with mucus-secreting glands (goblet cells in crypts). There are no villi

— a layer of circular muscle containing a nerve plexus

— a layer of longitudinal muscle partly arranged in three thick bands called taenia

— a serous coat of peritoneum which in some areas forms a mesentery.

Mucosa

Muscle wall

Diverticular disease (diverticulosis)

Diverticula (singular — diverticulum) are 'blow-outs' of the bowel mucosa at the weak places in the wall — between the taenia where the blood vessels enter. They are commoner on the left side of the colon, especially in the pelvis, and occur more frequently in older people. Their cause is unknown, but high pressure inside the bowel may be responsible, possibly due to disturbed motility and a diet deficient in fibre.

Retrocaecal appendix

Appendicitis is the commonest abdominal emergency needing surgery. It happens either because the lymphoid tissue swells and obstructs the lumen, or because faeces or a foreign body become impacted in it. The blood supply is then impaired, and the ischaemic tissues become infected. The inflammation may resolve, often with fibrosis and narrowing, so further attacks are likely. In other cases the infection may be localised by omentum to form an abscess, or the appendix may become gangrenous and perforate, causing generalised peritonitis.

Many people have no symptoms. Some develop diverticulitis (infection of pouch), because the wall has no muscle, cannot empty, and the contents stagnate.
In severe cases the inflamed diverticulum may:
— form an abscess
— perforate into the abdominal cavity, causing peritonitis
— penetrate into another organ, forming a fistula
— heal with fibrosis. The narrowed segment of bowel may form a mass or cause an obstruction, and thus mimic a carcinoma.
The most useful diagnostic test is the barium enema.
Treatment: mild cases of discomfort respond to increased fibre in the diet.
Acute diverticulitis is treated by rest, antibiotics and intravenous fluids.
Surgery is needed for complications.

Defaecation

1. In babies and small children, emptying of the bowel happens via a spinal reflex: when the rectum is distended, about half the large intestine empties.

2. As the child gets older and the nervous system becomes sufficiently mature, the process comes under voluntary control. When bowel contents distend the upper part of the rectum (the ampulla), its owner becomes aware of the fact and feels the desire to open the bowels.

3. On reaching the lavatory, defaecation begins as a willed action, though co-ordination of muscles is involuntary.

4. The longitudinal muscle of the bowel wall contracts, shortening the rectum.

5. Meanwhile the anal sphincter relaxes.

6. Then the circular muscle of the bowel wall constricts to form a moving contraction ring. This passes along the rectum, squeezing the faeces ahead of it down its length, along the canal and through the anus to the outside world.

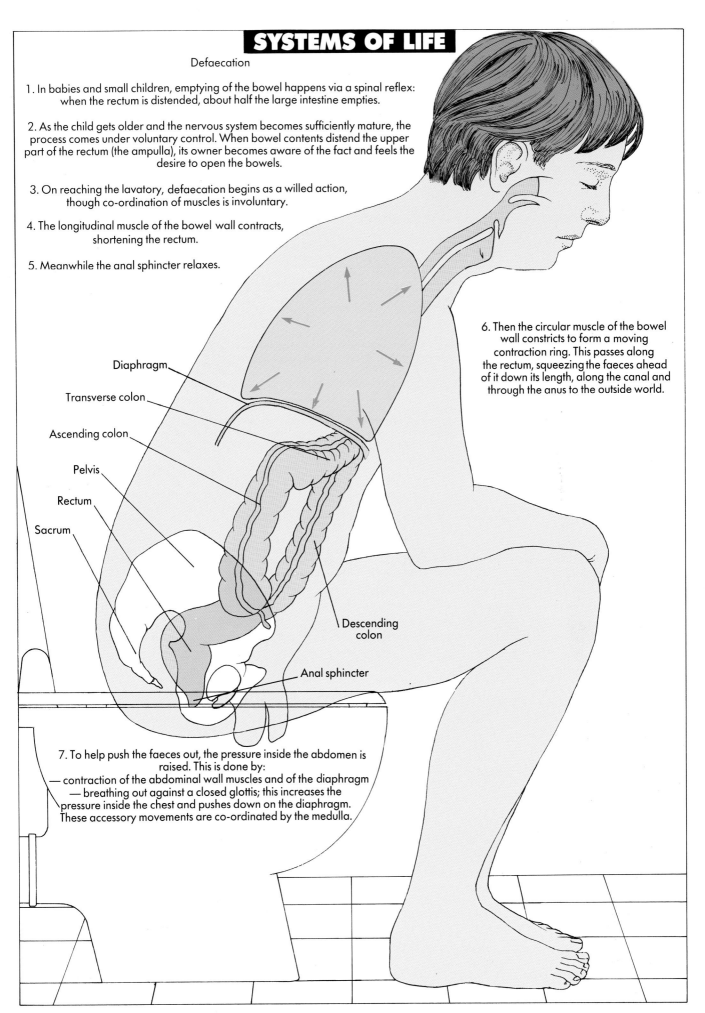

Diaphragm

Transverse colon

Ascending colon

Pelvis

Rectum

Sacrum

Descending colon

Anal sphincter

7. To help push the faeces out, the pressure inside the abdomen is raised. This is done by:
— contraction of the abdominal wall muscles and of the diaphragm
— breathing out against a closed glottis; this increases the pressure inside the chest and pushes down on the diaphragm. These accessory movements are co-ordinated by the medulla.

Bowel habit

How often a healthy person opens his or her bowels may vary from three times a day to three times a week. Most people know what is 'normal for them'; a change from the usual pattern is sometimes a sign of serious illness, and should be reported to the doctor.

Constipation

In this condition the bowels are opened very infrequently, and/or the stools are so hard that passing them is painful. Elderly patients are especially likely to become 'impacted' with large amounts of hard faeces. They may then develop 'spurious diarrhoea', as the faecal mass irritates the bowel lining, causing secretion of mucus which dissolves some stool and leaks past the blockage, causing soiling. Soft faeces can also build up and leak.

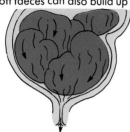

Common causes of constipation include:
— lack of dietary fibre
— unwanted effects of medicines, eg strong painkillers, antacids, antidepressants, hypotensives, iron.
When accompanied by rectal bleeding, carcinoma of the colon must be excluded. When appropriate, investigations continue to exclude rarer causes such as abnormality of the nerve supply to the bowel muscle (eg in Hirschsprung's disease or a prolapsed intervertebral disc) or hypothyroidism.
Treatment depends on the cause.

Colorectal carcinoma

This is very common, causing more than 16 000 deaths per year in the UK. It occurs most frequently in:
— people eating a low-fibre, high-fat Western diet
— people who have benign polyps which become malignant
— those with inflammatory bowel diseases such as ulcerative colitis.

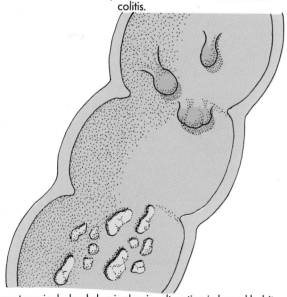

Symptoms include abdominal pain, alteration in bowel habit, rectal bleeding and the anaemia it causes. Investigations include the testing of stool for blood, proctoscopy, sigmoidoscopy and colonoscopy as appropriate to inspect and biopsy the bowel lining, and barium enema. If a cancer is found, the degree of spread can be assessed using an isotope scan of the liver. Treatment is surgical, involving the removal of the tumour and a surrounding margin of normal tissue. Up to 95% early cases (confined to bowel wall at diagnosis) survive for 5 years.

Diarrhoea

Excessive loss of fluid stools can lead to dehydration and loss of electrolytes, especially potassium. This can be dangerous in young children and old people. Very severe diarrhoea, as in untreated cholera, can kill previously healthy adults.
Acute diarrhoea is commonly caused by unwise eating or by infection with viruses, bacteria or amoebae. Chronic diarrhoea may be due to an 'irritable bowel', stress, bowel disease such as ulcerative colitis or cancer, malabsorption, thyroid over-activity or the unwanted effects of medicines, eg antibiotics, non-steroidal anti-inflammatory agents.
Treatment depends on the cause.

Stomas

These are artificial openings in the abdominal wall through which the bowel empties. There are three types:
— colostomy — temporary, allowing a diseased bowel to heal before the normal pattern is restored
— permanent, when part of the normal bowel pathway is removed, as is necessary in some cases of cancer
— ileostomy — when the opening is made higher up the bowel. This is necessary after total colectomy for severe ulcerative colitis
— urostomy — urine is drained to the outside world via a bowel loop.

Except in an emergency, the stoma and the reasons for it should be discussed with the patient and his relatives before the operation. The stoma care nurse can give expert advice and the patient is put in touch with the appropriate self-help organisation, such as the Colostomy Welfare Group or the Ileostomy Association.
The stoma opening must be formed away from the operation incision and away from bones, scars and skin creases. Whenever possible the patient's preferred activities and taste in clothes should be taken into account, so that the bag is inconspicuous in wear and does not get in the way.

Effects of digestive system disease on daily living

The main activities affected are eating and excretion. The change of body image following formation of a stoma may interfere with sexual activity; counselling may help.

SYSTEMS OF LIFE
The urinary system

The main functions of the kidneys are to keep normal blood constituents like water and electrolytes at healthy levels, and to eliminate waste products and foreign substances from the body. The urine the kidneys produce is tailored to the body's needs at the time it is formed. It then drains down the ureters into the bladder, where it is stored until it is convenient to pass it out through the urethra.

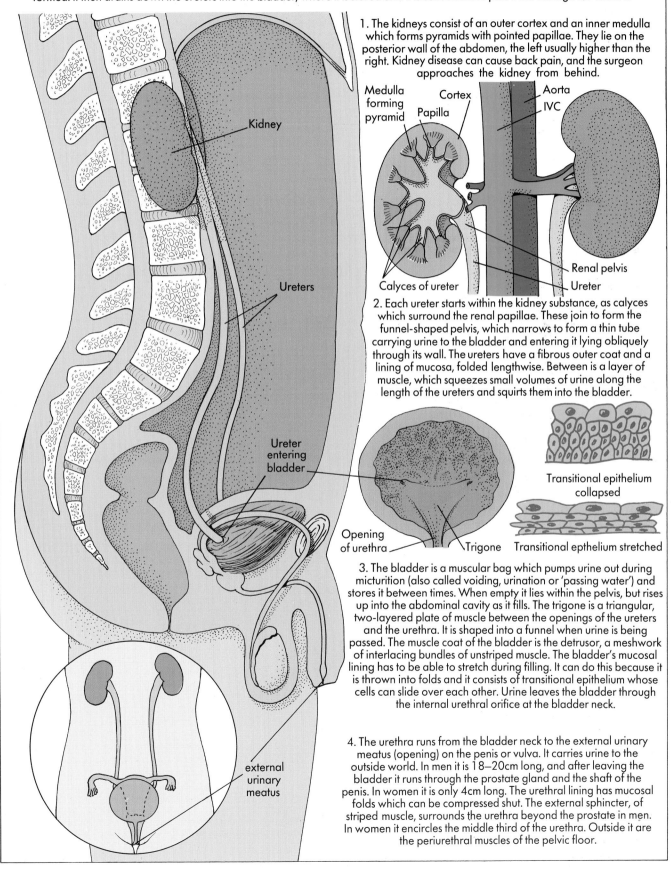

1. The kidneys consist of an outer cortex and an inner medulla which forms pyramids with pointed papillae. They lie on the posterior wall of the abdomen, the left usually higher than the right. Kidney disease can cause back pain, and the surgeon approaches the kidney from behind.

Medulla forming pyramid · Papilla · Cortex · Aorta · IVC · Calyces of ureter · Renal pelvis · Ureter

Kidney · Ureters · Ureter entering bladder · external urinary meatus

2. Each ureter starts within the kidney substance, as calyces which surround the renal papillae. These join to form the funnel-shaped pelvis, which narrows to form a thin tube carrying urine to the bladder and entering it lying obliquely through its wall. The ureters have a fibrous outer coat and a lining of mucosa, folded lengthwise. Between is a layer of muscle, which squeezes small volumes of urine along the length of the ureters and squirts them into the bladder.

Transitional epithelium collapsed

Opening of urethra · Trigone · Transitional epthelium stretched

3. The bladder is a muscular bag which pumps urine out during micturition (also called voiding, urination or 'passing water') and stores it between times. When empty it lies within the pelvis, but rises up into the abdominal cavity as it fills. The trigone is a triangular, two-layered plate of muscle between the openings of the ureters and the urethra. It is shaped into a funnel when urine is being passed. The muscle coat of the bladder is the detrusor, a meshwork of interlacing bundles of unstriped muscle. The bladder's mucosal lining has to be able to stretch during filling. It can do this because it is thrown into folds and it consists of transitional epithelium whose cells can slide over each other. Urine leaves the bladder through the internal urethral orifice at the bladder neck.

4. The urethra runs from the bladder neck to the external urinary meatus (opening) on the penis or vulva. It carries urine to the outside world. In men it is 18–20cm long, and after leaving the bladder it runs through the prostate gland and the shaft of the penis. In women it is only 4cm long. The urethral lining has mucosal folds which can be compressed shut. The external sphincter, of striped muscle, surrounds the urethra beyond the prostate in men. In women it encircles the middle third of the urethra. Outside it are the periurethral muscles of the pelvic floor.

SYSTEMS OF LIFE

The kidney's structure and how it works

The basic unit of the kidney is the nephron, consisting of the glomerulus and its tubule, draining into a collecting tubule. Down the length of the tubule the composition of the filtrate is adjusted to the body's needs. Waste from body metabolism or foreign substances like medicines are either filtered out of the blood by the glomerulus or are passed into the tubule. The altered filtrate thus eventually leaves the body as urine.

How the kidney works

The glomerular tufts of blood vessels are supplied by branches of the renal artery. The vessels leaving the glomerulus form capillary networks that run between the tubules. Substances can therefore pass across between the blood and the tubular fluid nearby. Blood in the glomerulus is filtered rather like straining peas in a colander. Blood cells and large molecules like most proteins stay behind in the blood vessel, while water and small molecules pass on into the renal tubule. The volume of fluid filtered by the glomerulus is less if the blood supply to the kidney is reduced — for instance in a patient who has lost blood. If the glomerulus is more permeable than normal, as in some types of kidney disease, protein molecules may escape into the tubule and eventually appear in the urine.

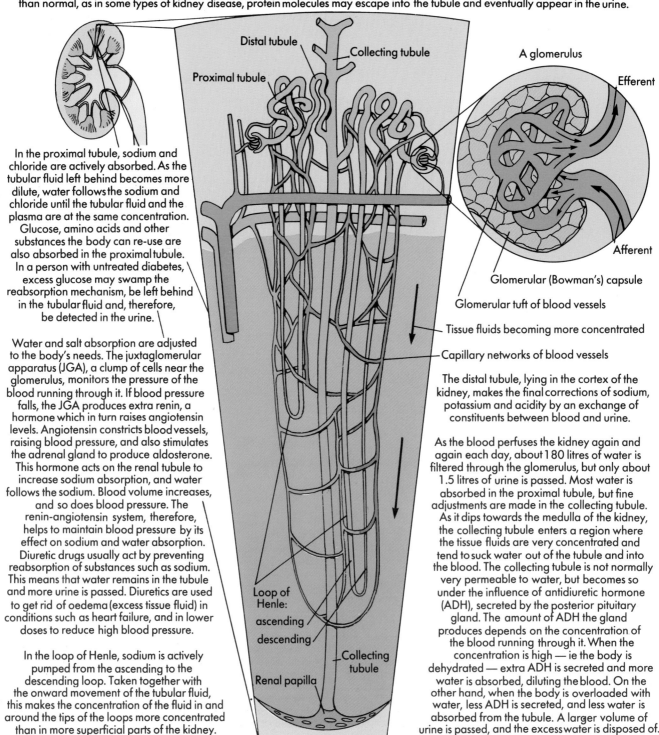

Distal tubule

Collecting tubule

Proximal tubule

A glomerulus

Efferent

Afferent

Glomerular (Bowman's) capsule

Glomerular tuft of blood vessels

Tissue fluids becoming more concentrated

Capillary networks of blood vessels

Loop of Henle:
ascending
descending

Collecting tubule

Renal papilla

In the proximal tubule, sodium and chloride are actively absorbed. As the tubular fluid left behind becomes more dilute, water follows the sodium and chloride until the tubular fluid and the plasma are at the same concentration. Glucose, amino acids and other substances the body can re-use are also absorbed in the proximal tubule. In a person with untreated diabetes, excess glucose may swamp the reabsorption mechanism, be left behind in the tubular fluid and, therefore, be detected in the urine.

Water and salt absorption are adjusted to the body's needs. The juxtaglomerular apparatus (JGA), a clump of cells near the glomerulus, monitors the pressure of the blood running through it. If blood pressure falls, the JGA produces extra renin, a hormone which in turn raises angiotensin levels. Angiotensin constricts blood vessels, raising blood pressure, and also stimulates the adrenal gland to produce aldosterone. This hormone acts on the renal tubule to increase sodium absorption, and water follows the sodium. Blood volume increases, and so does blood pressure. The renin-angiotensin system, therefore, helps to maintain blood pressure by its effect on sodium and water absorption. Diuretic drugs usually act by preventing reabsorption of substances such as sodium. This means that water remains in the tubule and more urine is passed. Diuretics are used to get rid of oedema (excess tissue fluid) in conditions such as heart failure, and in lower doses to reduce high blood pressure.

In the loop of Henle, sodium is actively pumped from the ascending to the descending loop. Taken together with the onward movement of the tubular fluid, this makes the concentration of the fluid in and around the tips of the loops more concentrated than in more superficial parts of the kidney.

The distal tubule, lying in the cortex of the kidney, makes the final corrections of sodium, potassium and acidity by an exchange of constituents between blood and urine.

As the blood perfuses the kidney again and again each day, about 180 litres of water is filtered through the glomerulus, but only about 1.5 litres of urine is passed. Most water is absorbed in the proximal tubule, but fine adjustments are made in the collecting tubule. As it dips towards the medulla of the kidney, the collecting tubule enters a region where the tissue fluids are very concentrated and tend to suck water out of the tubule and into the blood. The collecting tubule is not normally very permeable to water, but becomes so under the influence of antidiuretic hormone (ADH), secreted by the posterior pituitary gland. The amount of ADH the gland produces depends on the concentration of the blood running through it. When the concentration is high — ie the body is dehydrated — extra ADH is secreted and more water is absorbed, diluting the blood. On the other hand, when the body is overloaded with water, less ADH is secreted, and less water is absorbed from the tubule. A larger volume of urine is passed, and the excess water is disposed of.

Control of micturition — how urinary continence is maintained: (simplified)

1. In babies and small children a simple spinal reflex controls the passage of urine. As the bladder fills, the pressure inside it rises and stretch receptors in its wall fire impulses up nerve pathways to the spinal cord.

2. The nerves then carry impulses back to the detrusor muscle of the bladder.

3. This then contracts, raising the pressure inside the bladder and pulling the bladder neck open.

4. Urine then runs into the posterior urethra. Sensory receptors detect it and a further reflex action relaxes the external sphincter. Urine can then be passed.

5. As the child's nervous system matures, the sensation of bladder fullness is carried up the spinal cord until it eventually reaches the cortical centres in the frontal lobes. Here it reaches consciousness, and the person becomes aware of the filling bladder.

6. If it is not convenient to pass urine, the reflex is inhibited. The detrusor muscle does not contract but stretches, so the bladder enlarges and can hold more urine. The stretch receptors are no longer stimulated, and the desire to pass urine goes away for the time being.

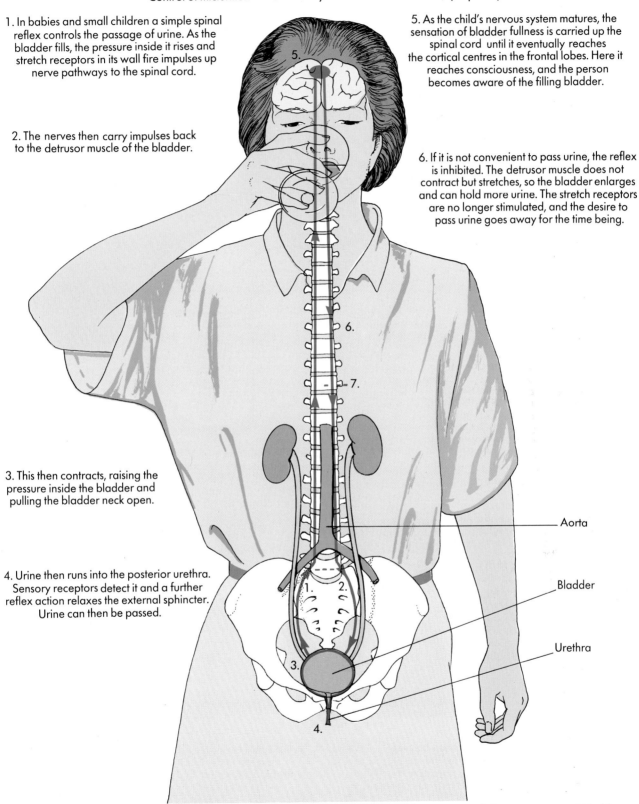

Aorta

Bladder

Urethra

7. As the bladder continues to fill, the stretch receptors are again stimulated and the person again becomes aware of bladder fullness. Emptying may again by inhibited for a time, but eventually the rise in pressure becomes painful. When the person decides to empty the bladder, the inhibition is switched off like removing a brake, and urine is passed. Urine flow is helped if the muscles of the pelvic floor are relaxed and intra-abdominal pressure is raised by contraction of the diaphragm and the abdominal wall muscles; this pushes down on the bladder and opens the urine pathway.

Most cases of urinary incontinence have a number of interacting causes. This can be identified by careful history-taking, examination and investigations. An appropriate treatment programme can then be devised.

SYSTEMS OF LIFE

Urine is commonly tested for:

Protein: normally little or none is found. Excess may be due to kidney disease, urinary infection or contamination by vaginal discharge. If found, an MSU should be obtained.

Blood: normal urine contains none. It may appear because of bladder or prostate cancer, benign tumours, infection or stones. Patients with proven haematuria are referred to an urologist.

Glucose: glycosuria (glucose in urine) may indicate a raised blood sugar and be a sign of diabetes. Sometimes sugar spills over into the urine even though the blood level is normal — a low renal threshold. If glucose is found in the urine the blood glucose should be checked.

Other tests (eg for bile or ketones) can be performed if thought to be necessary.

The midstream urine specimen (MSU)

The patient carefully cleans round his or her urethral meatus with normal saline and swabs. He or she then passes some urine, stopping before the bladder is empty. This urine washes out the lower urinary tract, and is thrown away. Urine is next passed into the sterile container as the clean midstream specimen; any remaining urine can be discarded. If the specimen is properly taken, cells and organisms found in it indicate the true state of affairs in the bladder and upper urinary tract.

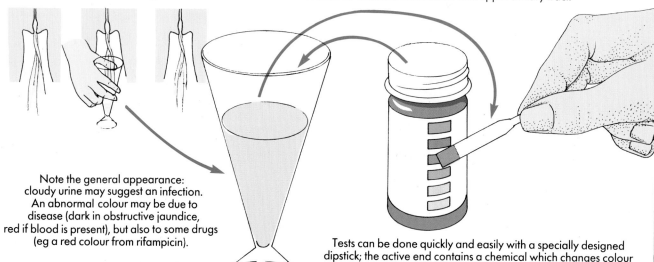

Note the general appearance: cloudy urine may suggest an infection. An abnormal colour may be due to disease (dark in obstructive jaundice, red if blood is present), but also to some drugs (eg a red colour from rifampicin).

Tests can be done quickly and easily with a specially designed dipstick; the active end contains a chemical which changes colour when it meets the substance tested for. Errors can occur if the urine has been stored in a contaminated container, or if the stick colour is compared with the colour chart at the wrong time.

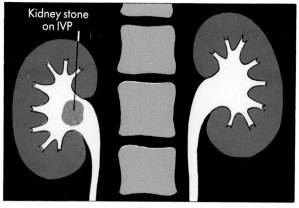

Renal imaging

Pictures of the urinary tract can be obtained
— by the use of contrast medium: injected into the blood or concentrated by the kidney (intravenous pyelogram — IVP) or injected into the tract — antegrade or retrograde pyelography
— by ultrasound
— by isotope scans
— by computed tomograph (CT) scans or magnetic resonance imaging (MRI)

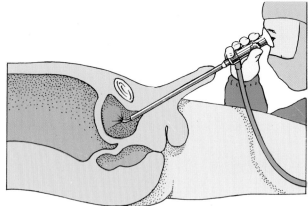

Cystoscopy

A fine light-bearing telescope is passed up the urethra into the bladder under local or general anaesthesia. Then:
— the bladder, urethra and ureteric openings can be examined and tissue samples taken if necessary
— fine-bore catheters can be passed up the ureters for urine sampling or contrast injection
— some operations can be performed, eg transurethral resection of prostate, removal of foreign bodies from the bladder.

Effect of urinary tract disease on daily living activities

Incontinence of urine or the fear of it can restrict the sufferer's activities and ruin social and sexual life.

Chronic renal failure causes general ill health, ending in death if untreated. Renal transplantation provides the best quality of life.

SYSTEMS OF LIFE
Reproductive system — Part 1

Cell

Nucleus   Cytoplasm

Chromosomes formed
of coiled coils of DNA
in a protein sheath

DNA spiral
of genes

The function of the reproductive system is to produce new human beings. The gonads — the male testes and female ovaries — produce gametes: male sperm, female ova (singular: ovum). The nuclei of the gametes contain information about personal characteristics: height, blood group, eye colour and so on. This is chemically coded as genes on chromosomes. If a sperm succeeds in fertilising an ovum after intercourse, the nuclei of the two gametes fuse. The new nucleus so formed contains the genetic specifications for the new person. Though all the genes come from the two parents, the assortment is different each time fertilisation happens.

Sex Differentiation

Genetic sex is determined at conception: females receive an X chromosome from each parent, while males get an X from the mother and a Y from the father. If the embryo has a Y chromosome, a testis develops; without a Y, an ovary is formed. The sex of the gonad then influences the sex of the developing sex organs (genitalia); male hormones from a testis or elsewhere produce male genitalia, while female organs develop if male hormones are absent.

Mother
X X

Father
X Y

(X) ova (X)   (X) sperm (Y)

FERTILISATION

X X
Female

X Y
Male

Ovary

Testis

Female genitals

Male genitals

	Normal		Turner's/ Klinefelter's (Simplified)			
Parents	XX	XY	XX		XY	
Gametes	X X	X Y	X X	O	XY	
Offspring	XY or XX		XO	XO	XXY	XXY
			Turner's		Klinefelter's	

Turner's syndrome and Klinefelter's syndrome happen when the sex chromosomes fail to separate properly during cell division. This is called 'non-disjunction'.

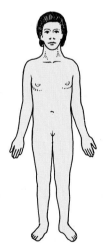

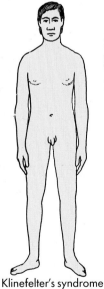

Turner's syndrome
One X chromosome is missing, so the baby's sex chromosomes are XO rather than XX. Many Turner's fetuses abort spontaneously. Those that survive usually have underdeveloped ovaries, do not experience puberty and are nearly always infertile. They may also be short in stature, with a webbed neck, angled elbows (cubitus valgus), a shield-shaped chest and short 4th metacarpals. 10–20% patients have coarctation of the aorta or aortic valve lesions. Treatment: Female hormones are given to produce a feminine appearance, normal vaginal lubrication and thus comfortable intercourse, and to prevent osteoporosis.

Klinefelter's syndrome
The baby has an extra X chromosome, XXY rather than XX or XY. His testicles fail to develop, and produce few sperm and scanty male hormones. Lacking testosterone, an adult man with Klinefelter's tends to have small genitals, less hair on his face or body and a higher pitched voice than is usual. He tends to be taller than average, but less muscular. Milder cases may be diagnosed during investigations for infertility. Klinefelter's patients tend to gain weight easily. Treatment: some patients opt for regular testosterone injections, which deepen the voice and make the appearance more masculine. Excess weight gain may lead to diabetes, thrombophlebitis and other complications, so should be avoided.

Male Reproductive System

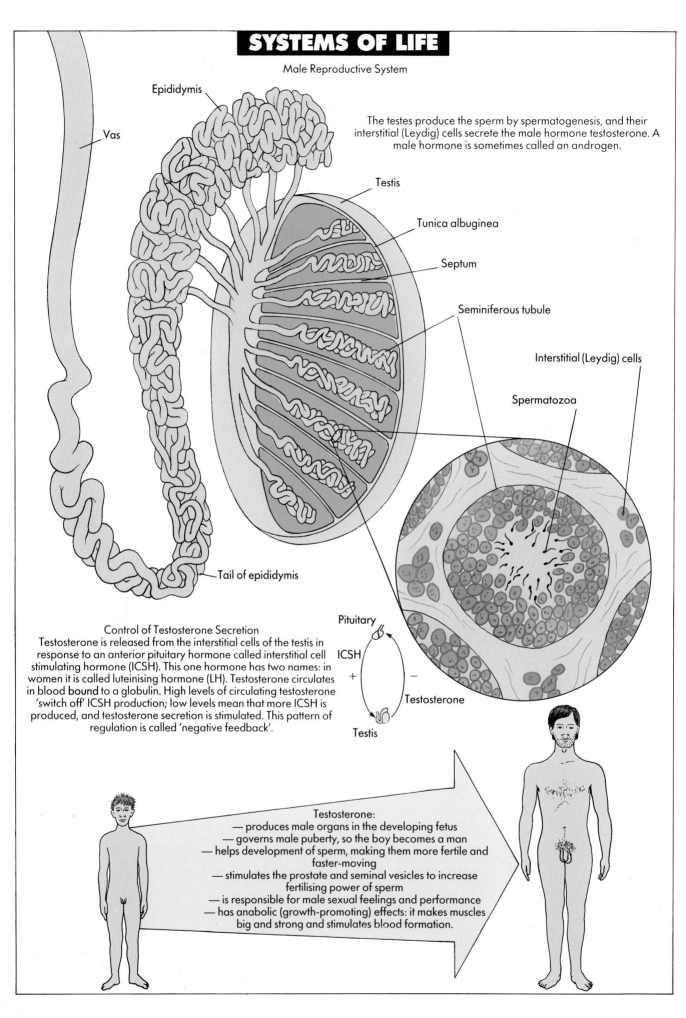

Epididymis

Vas

The testes produce the sperm by spermatogenesis, and their interstitial (Leydig) cells secrete the male hormone testosterone. A male hormone is sometimes called an androgen.

Testis

Tunica albuginea

Septum

Seminiferous tubule

Interstitial (Leydig) cells

Spermatozoa

Tail of epididymis

Control of Testosterone Secretion
Testosterone is released from the interstitial cells of the testis in response to an anterior pituitary hormone called interstitial cell stimulating hormone (ICSH). This one hormone has two names: in women it is called luteinising hormone (LH). Testosterone circulates in blood **bound** to a globulin. High levels of circulating testosterone 'switch off' ICSH production; low levels mean that more ICSH is produced, and testosterone secretion is stimulated. This pattern of regulation is called 'negative feedback'.

Pituitary

ICSH

+

−

Testosterone

Testis

Testosterone:
— produces male organs in the developing fetus
— governs male puberty, so the boy becomes a man
— helps development of sperm, making them more fertile and faster-moving
— stimulates the prostate and seminal vesicles to increase fertilising power of sperm
— is responsible for male sexual feelings and performance
— has anabolic (growth-promoting) effects: it makes muscles big and strong and stimulates blood formation.

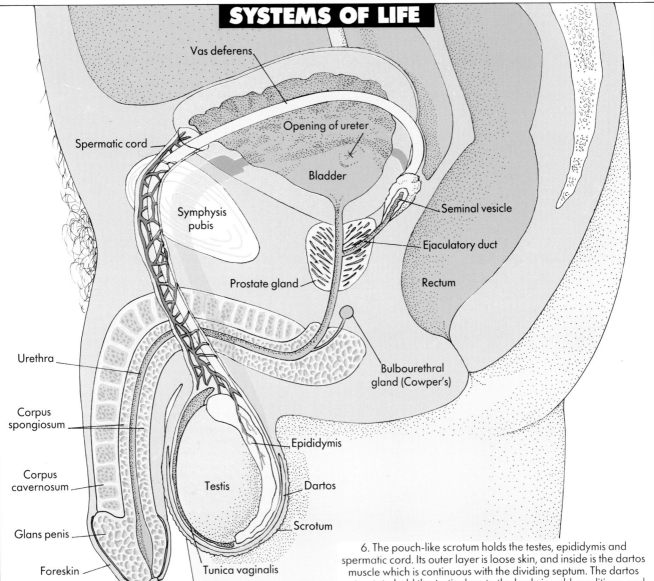

Vas deferens

Opening of ureter

Spermatic cord

Bladder

Symphysis pubis

Seminal vesicle

Ejaculatory duct

Prostate gland

Rectum

Urethra

Bulbourethral gland (Cowper's)

Corpus spongiosum

Epididymis

Corpus cavernosum

Dartos

Testis

Glans penis

Scrotum

Foreskin

Tunica vaginalis

1. Sperm are carried from the testis to the outside world along a series of tubes. The first of these is the epididymis. This would be 6 metres long if it were stretched out fully; instead it is coiled and folded into a comma shape which is hooked **above** and behind the testis. Its tail opens into the vas deferens.

2. The vas has a thick muscular wall. On either side it runs upwards and joins the duct of the seminal vesicle to form the ejaculatory duct.

3. The ejaculatory duct is 2cm long and delivers its contents into the urethra as it runs through the prostate.

4. The prostate gland lies at the base of the bladder, surrounding the urethra and the ejaculatory ducts as they open into it. It is about the size and shape of a chestnut and is enclosed by a fibrous capsule. It consists of glandular tissue and muscle, and its small ducts drain into the urethra.

5. The two pea-sized bulbourethral (Cowper's) glands lie on either side of the urethra and pass their mucoid secretion into it.

Semen consists of sperm plus the secretions of the seminal vesicles, prostate and bulbourethral glands. These secretions add volume and may prolong **sperm** life. Semen is ejaculated at orgasm by contractions of the seminal vesicles, prostate and vas deferens.

Vasectomy is the operation in which the vas is cut and its two ends are separated and blocked. A few weeks after the operation the man becomes sterile, ie unable to father children. His potency — the ability to have erections and orgasms — is not affected.

6. The pouch-like scrotum holds the testes, epididymis and spermatic cord. Its outer layer is loose skin, and inside is the dartos muscle which is continuous with the dividing septum. The dartos contracts to hold the testis close to the body in cold conditions, and relaxes when it is warm. This is to keep the testis at the best temperature for making sperm. The dartos encloses the spermatic cord and its coverings.

During embryonic life the testis migrates from its formation site inside the abdomen near the kidney, downwards and outwards through the inguinal canal. It drags its nerves, vessels and the vas deferens behind it and pushes the layers of the abdominal wall in front. This is how the spermatic cord is formed and acquires its coverings.

The scrotum is lined by the outer layer of the double tunica vaginalis. The two layers are lubricated by fluid and allow the testis to slide about inside the scrotum, so that it is less easily injured.

7. Three masses of erectile tissue form the bulk of the penis. During an erection these become distended by blood, so the man's penis becomes stiff enough to penetrate the woman's vagina and deposit its sperm high up in it. There are two corpora cavernosa and one corpus spongiosum, with the penile part of the urethra running through it. At its distal end — the end farthest from the body — the corpus spongiosum enlarges to form the glans penis, with the urethra opening at its tip. The skin over the penis is loose enough to allow room for erection, and a fold of it, the foreskin or prepuce, **partially** covers the glans; it can then be retracted for washing.

Circumcision is the removal of most of the foreskin; risks include severe bleeding and damage to the penis. It may be performed for racial or religious reasons; the few medical indications include recurrent balanitis (infection beneath it) and paraphimosis (a tight foreskin is forced back into a painful constricting ring).

Swellings in and near the scrotum

These have many causes. Simple palpation can often help in diagnosis. Points to note are:
— what the swelling feels like: hard, soft, craggy, cystic, etc.
— whether the testis can be felt to be separate from the swelling
— whether the examining hand can 'get above' the swelling, ie, whether its upper limit is outside the abdomen

Common swellings include:

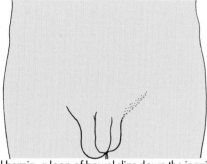

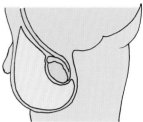

Hydrocele: fluid accumulates between the two layers of the tunica vaginalis, enclosing the testis which cannot be felt separately. The swelling is smooth, elastic and translucent to bright light. Its upper margin can be felt. Treatment: the sac of the hydrocele is surgically removed. In an unfit patient the fluid may be sucked out with a syringe and wide-bore needle. However, it usually reaccumulates, so tapping must be repeated.

Inguinal hernia: a loop of bowel slips down the inguinal canal, following all or part of the path taken by the testis during fetal life. The swelling is soft, the examining hand cannot feel its upper limit and the testis can be felt separately from it. Treatment: the bowel loop is replaced in the abdomen, ie the hernia is 'reduced', and its exit route blocked to prevent recurrence. Patients who are unfit or unwilling for surgery are supplied with a truss, whose pad aims to keep the hernia 'reduced'. Surgery is better whenever possible, as the truss is not usually efficient enough to stop the bowel loop from slipping far enough to risk obstruction or becoming 'strangulated' — ie losing its blood supply and becoming gangrenous

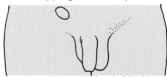

Maldescended testis: a testis may be 'left behind' anywhere along its migratory path: a common site is near the internal inguinal ring. A maldescended testis does not form sperm properly, perhaps because it is too warm. It is also more vulnerable to injury and more likely to become cancerous than one in the normal position. Treatment: orchidopexy, ie replacing and fixing the testis in the scrotum; this needs to be done in early childhood if the testis is to function normally later. If left too late, the useless maldescended testis is removed so that it cannot become malignant.

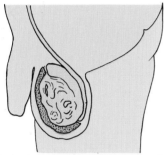

Tumours of the testis: the testis itself becomes enlarged, hard, craggy, heavy and insensitive to pain. Treatment: the testis is removed with its tumour (orchidectomy). Afterwards the patient has **radiotherapy** and/or chemotherapy, depending on individual circumstances.

The prostate

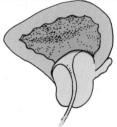

Benign prostatic hypertrophy (BPH) is a common cause of a frequent need to pass water urgently, a poor stream and sometimes incontinence. Urine may pool in a distended bladder (chronic retention) until it cannot be passed at all (acute on chronic retention). Treatment: surgical, either through a resectoscope (transurethral resection) or by open operation (retropubic prostatectomy).

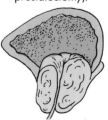

Torsion of the testis (twisting on the spermatic cord): this most often happens in a child or adolescent with an abnormally shaped or maldescended testis. The patient has severe abdominal pain and vomiting, and his testis and scrotum are swollen, painful and tender. Treatment: in early cases the testis can be untwisted and fixed to prevent recurrence; if diagnosed late the testis is usually already gangrenous because its blood supply has been twisted off. It then has to be removed.

Cancer of the prostate, common in old men, may grow slowly. It can cause symptoms like those of BPH and be found by chance at operation, or later spread to the bones causing pain. Treatment: observation for early cases; otherwise surgery, radiotherapy or hormone therapy. Prostatic cancer depends on male hormones for growth, so treatment aims to deprive it of these, either by castration (removal of both testes) or by using drugs which reduce testosterone levels.

SYSTEMS OF LIFE
Reproductive system — Part 2

Female Reproductive System

1. The female gonads are the two almond-shaped ovaries. The ova are formed during fetal life, so the baby girl is born with all the ova she will later need.

2. Nearby are the funnel-shaped, fringed, free ends of the uterine (Fallopian) tubes. The other ends are implanted into the uterus. The tubes are muscular and are lined by a ciliated mucous membrane which creates a current running towards the uterus.

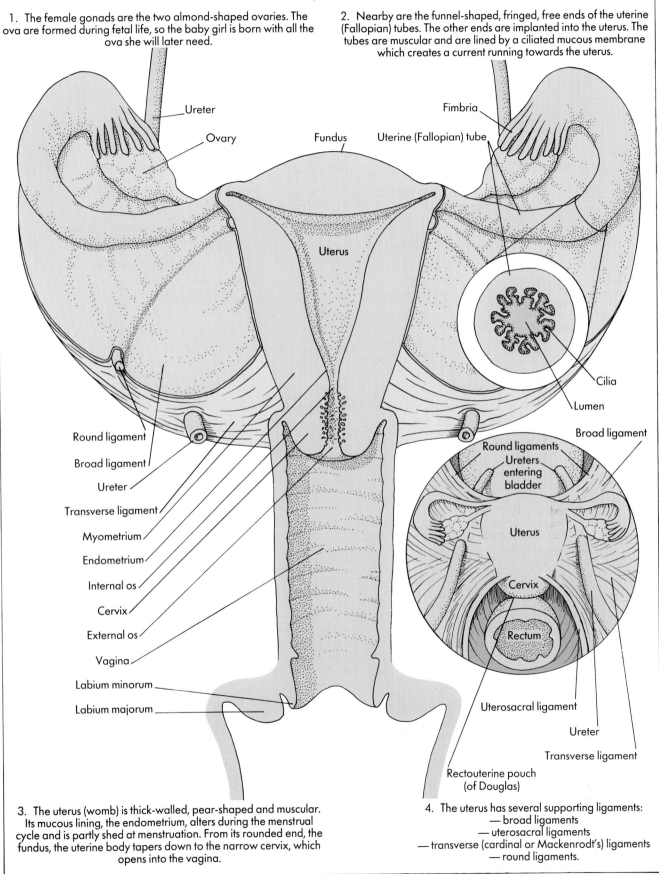

Ureter
Ovary
Fundus
Fimbria
Uterine (Fallopian) tube
Uterus
Cilia
Lumen
Round ligament
Broad ligament
Ureter
Transverse ligament
Myometrium
Endometrium
Internal os
Cervix
External os
Vagina
Labium minorum
Labium majorum
Broad ligament
Round ligaments
Ureters entering bladder
Uterus
Cervix
Rectum
Uterosacral ligament
Ureter
Transverse ligament
Rectouterine pouch (of Douglas)

3. The uterus (womb) is thick-walled, pear-shaped and muscular. Its mucous lining, the endometrium, alters during the menstrual cycle and is partly shed at menstruation. From its rounded end, the fundus, the uterine body tapers down to the narrow cervix, which opens into the vagina.

4. The uterus has several supporting ligaments:
— broad ligaments
— uterosacral ligaments
— transverse (cardinal or Mackenrodt's) ligaments
— round ligaments.

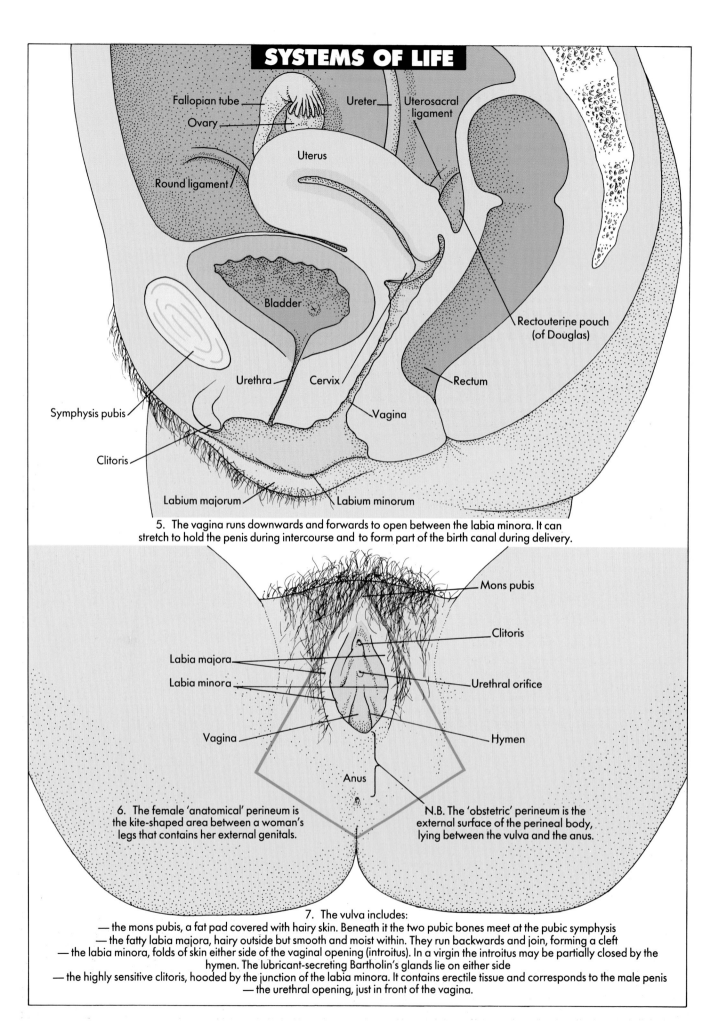

Fallopian tube
Ovary
Ureter
Uterosacral ligament
Uterus
Round ligament
Bladder
Rectouterine pouch (of Douglas)
Urethra
Cervix
Rectum
Symphysis pubis
Vagina
Clitoris
Labium majorum
Labium minorum

5. The vagina runs downwards and forwards to open between the labia minora. It can stretch to hold the penis during intercourse and to form part of the birth canal during delivery.

Mons pubis
Clitoris
Labia majora
Urethral orifice
Labia minora
Vagina
Hymen
Anus

6. The female 'anatomical' perineum is the kite-shaped area between a woman's legs that contains her external genitals.

N.B. The 'obstetric' perineum is the external surface of the perineal body, lying between the vulva and the anus.

7. The vulva includes:
— the mons pubis, a fat pad covered with hairy skin. Beneath it the two pubic bones meet at the pubic symphysis
— the fatty labia majora, hairy outside but smooth and moist within. They run backwards and join, forming a cleft
— the labia minora, folds of skin either side of the vaginal opening (introitus). In a virgin the introitus may be partially closed by the hymen. The lubricant-secreting Bartholin's glands lie on either side
— the highly sensitive clitoris, hooded by the junction of the labia minora. It contains erectile tissue and corresponds to the male penis
— the urethral opening, just in front of the vagina.

SYSTEMS OF LIFE

The menstrual cycle

The pituitary gland and ovary control the changes in the uterine lining (endometrium).

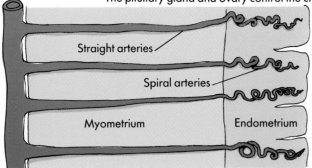

1. Menstruation

The cycle is timed from the first day of the menstrual bleed, as day 1. The endometrium has straight arteries to its deep layers and spiral arteries more superficially. During menstruation, groups of spiral arteries go into spasm. The part of endometrium normally supplied by the contracted vessels then dies for lack of a blood supply. When the arteries relax again, blood is shed through the damaged capillary walls. Mixed with scraps of sloughed endometrium and mucus secreted by the glands, it runs down the vagina as menstrual fluid. The rest of the spiral arteries go into spasm in turn, a few at a time. This results in intermittent blood loss over 3–6 days, the menstrual period. Periods start at puberty — the menarche. They recur until the menopause, usually between the ages of 45 and 55, with interruptions during pregnancy and lactation.

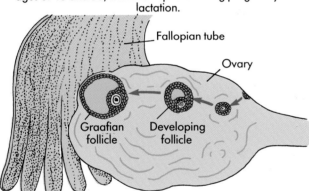

2. The proliferative phase

This lasts from the end of menstruation to the time of ovulation. Follicle-stimulating hormone (FSH) from the anterior pituitary stimulates an ovarian (Graafian) follicle to grow and mature around the developing ovum. The follicle produces increasing amounts of the oestrogen oestradiol. This hormone stimulates the endometrium to grow and proliferate.

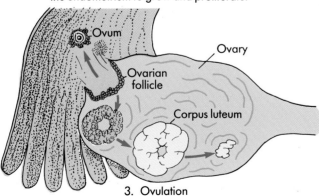

3. Ovulation

The amount of oestradiol produced in the ovarian follicle 'feeds back' to the pituitary. When the oestradiol level peaks, pituitary FSH is 'switched off', and there is a sudden surge of pituitary LH (luteinising hormone). This causes ovulation: the distended follicle bursts through to the surface of the ovary and the ovum pops out. The burst and collapsed follicle then becomes the corpus luteum. Ovulation cannot happen without a spike of LH.

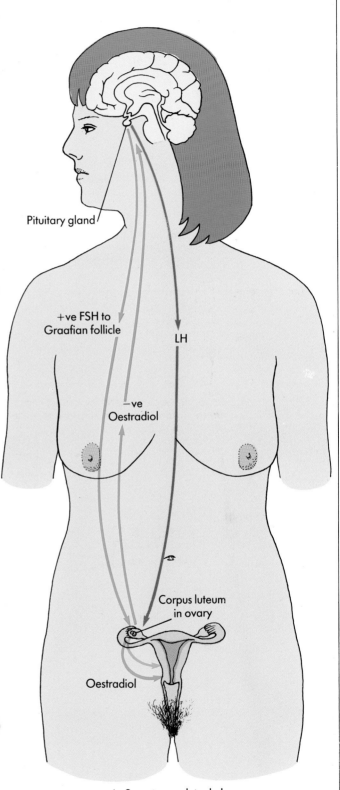

4. Secretory or luteal phase

The corpus luteum produces rising amounts of the hormones oestradiol and progesterone. These act on the endometrium to produce a bed for implantation of a possible pregnancy. The glands hypertrophy and the arteries become spiral.

5a. Pregnancy occurs

If the ovum is fertilised, it travels down the Fallopian tube into the uterus, where it burrows into the prepared endometrium. The tissues between the ovum and uterine wall which will later form the placenta now produce human chorionic gonadotrophin (HCG). HCG keeps the corpus luteum functioning for the first three months of pregnancy, while its hormones are needed. After this time the placenta is sufficiently developed to take over hormone production, and the corpus luteum degenerates.

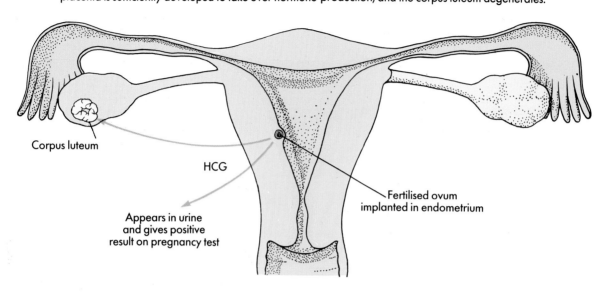

Corpus luteum

HCG

Appears in urine
and gives positive
result on pregnancy test

Fertilised ovum
implanted in endometrium

5b. No pregnancy — the ovum remains unfertilised

The hormones from the corpus luteum 'feed back' to the anterior pituitary and 'switch off' its hormones. Without either these or the HCG from a successful pregnancy, the corpus luteum cannot survive. Once it degenerates and its hormones are lacking, the endometrial spiral arteries go into periodic shut-down. Menstruation follows, and the cycle starts again.

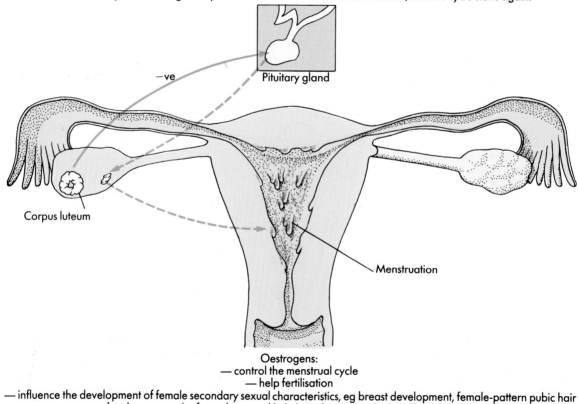

−ve

Pituitary gland

Corpus luteum

Menstruation

Oestrogens:
— control the menstrual cycle
— help fertilisation
— influence the development of female secondary sexual characteristics, eg breast development, female-pattern pubic hair
— slow bone growth after puberty and help keep bone mass high until the menopause
— cause salt and water retention
— make the blood more likely to clot in some circumstances

SYSTEMS OF LIFE
Reproductive system — Part 3

Sexual Response

1. Many things — thoughts, sights, sounds and physical sensations — can create sexual excitement. During lovemaking it can be increased by 'foreplay', ie caressing some parts of the body: such 'erogenous zones' include the nipples in women and some men, and the external genitalia in both sexes. During this stage:

— heart rate and blood pressure rise, the skin flushes over the head, neck and face, the nipples erect and the breasts swell

— the penis erects and the cremaster muscle contracts, pulling up the testes

— the clitoris erects and the labia engorge and separate, opening the vaginal entrance

— the vagina relaxes and its glands lubricate it. The genital changes help the man to slide his penis into the woman's waiting vagina, after which both partners make back-and-forth pelvic thrusting movements.

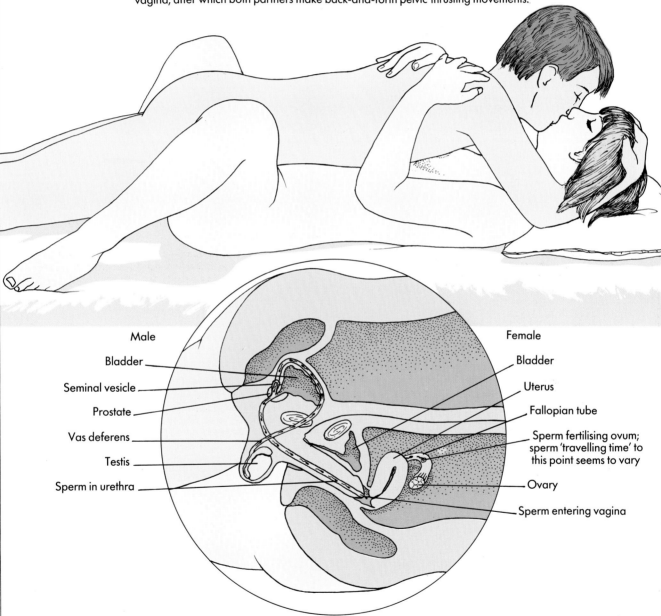

Male
- Bladder
- Seminal vesicle
- Prostate
- Vas deferens
- Testis
- Sperm in urethra

Female
- Bladder
- Uterus
- Fallopian tube
- Sperm fertilising ovum; sperm 'travelling time' to this point seems to vary
- Ovary
- Sperm entering vagina

2. At orgasm the man's seminal vesicles, prostate and urethra contract, depositing his semen high in the woman's vagina. The woman does not always have an orgasm during intercourse. If she does so after her partner, then the rhythmic orgasmic contractions of her uterus and vagina may suck up sperm through the cervical canal from the seminal pool in the vagina around the cervical os; this may help the sperm on their way towards the ovum.

3. After orgasm, the erections of clitoris and penis subside and the testes fall to their usual position in the relaxed scrotum. The skin and nipple changes disappear and heart rate and blood pressure return to normal. In men there is a refractory phase before he can start again; this does not seem to occur in women.

NB. Human sexual behaviour involves far more than basic anatomy and physiology; to understand and help patients with this aspect of their lives, it is sensible to read widely.

Signs of Pregnancy

Tests for pregnancy are performed on the mother's urine. They detect human chorionic gonadotrophin produced by the developing placenta.

Nausea and vomiting, 'morning sickness', may in fact occur at any time of the day.

Changes in the breasts:
swelling, tenderness, veins becoming more obvious.
The areolae darken and their tubercles become more prominent.

Nipple

Areola   Tubercles

Amenorrhoea (missing periods)

Enlargement of uterus: it can be felt rising into the abdomen from around the twelfth week. The muscle fibres enlarge greatly and uterine weight increases from about 30 grams to 1000g by term.

Frequency of micturition and constipation.

Changes in the mother's body help the baby's growth and development:

— respiration becomes more efficient to provide more oxygen

— cardiac output rises, blood volume increases and the blood carries more oxygen to the uterus and the fetus inside it. The fetus has high-uptake fetal haemoglobin to make the most of the oxygen supply

— extra fat is laid down to provide a reservoir of energy for breastfeeding

— calcium, iron and folate are made available for the baby's bones and blood.

SYSTEMS OF LIFE

Placenta — this develops where the ovum implants, usually high in the body of the uterus.
It is partly derived from fetal tissues and partly from the mother's uterine lining

Functions of placenta. It:
— produces hormones: human chorionic gonadotrophin in early pregnancy, falling later, and afterwards oestradiol and progesterone. It also influences hormone production by the corpus luteum and the adrenal cortex of both mother and baby

— supplies oxygen and nourishment to the fetus

— carries away fetal waste.

Pregnancy lasts about 280 days (40 weeks), dated from the beginning of the last period. The time is divided into three 'trimesters' of approximately three months each. No one knows exactly what starts labour off.

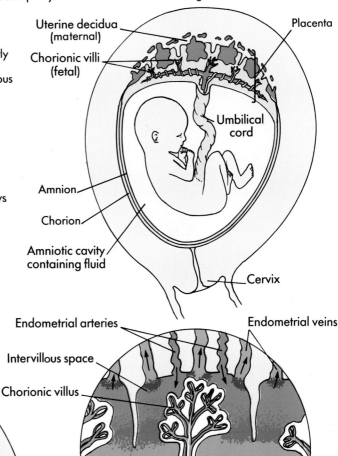

Amniotic fluid
This is secreted by branches of the umbilical vein. The amniotic cavity containing the fluid appears before the mother misses a period; by the time the baby is born, there are 500 — 1000ml of fluid. It surrounds the fetus and:

— cushions it against injury

— allows it to move easily, as in a hydrotherapy pool

— protects it against temperature changes

— helps to pass substances between mother and fetus

— provides the baby with fluid to drink, probably allowing 'sucking practice' before birth.

Turnover of fluid is rapid. Some is absorbed directly back into the placenta, while some is swallowed by the fetus and absorbed into its circulation before being excreted by the kidneys and passed back as urine. Eventually, fluid may be lost at the onset of labour ('the waters breaking'), while the rest gushes out as the baby is born.

Amniocentesis samples the fluid. This is most commonly done to diagnose Down's syndrome by examining the chromosomes in the baby's shed cells.

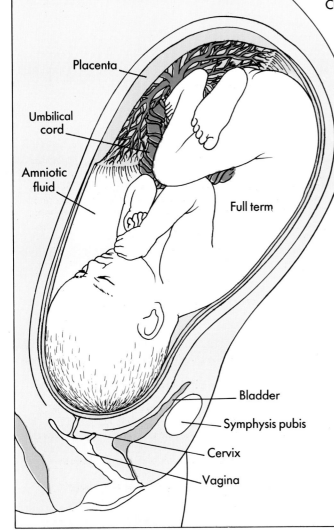

The Breast

The breasts consist of fat enclosing glandular tissue, which is arranged in lobes. Each lobe has lobules of milk-producing alveoli which drain into lactiferous ducts. These open on the areola, the pigmented area round the nipple. Beneath the areola the lactiferous ducts dilate to form lactiferous sinuses, which are compressed by the baby's gums when he or she sucks. The ducts narrow again to open directly on the nipple, rather like the holes on the rose of a watering can. Myoepithelial cells around the alveoli squeeze them, and muscle fibres encircling the nipples can erect them. The good nerve supply of the nipples is important both in lovemaking and in breastfeeding.

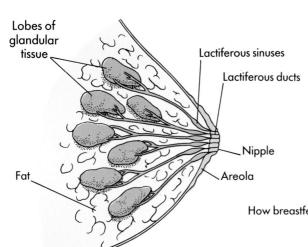

Lobes of glandular tissue

Lactiferous sinuses

Lactiferous ducts

Nipple

Areola

Fat

How breastfeeding works

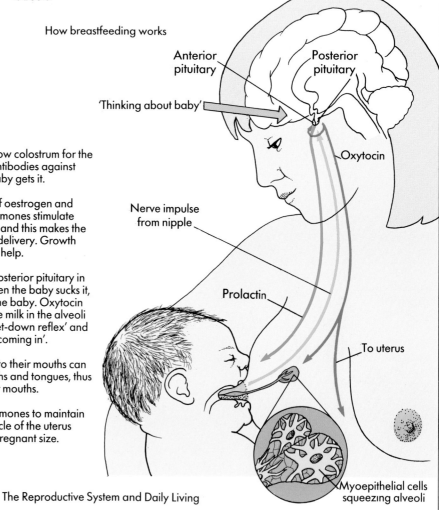

Anterior pituitary

Posterior pituitary

'Thinking about baby'

Oxytocin

Nerve impulse from nipple

Prolactin

To uterus

Myoepithelial cells squeezing alveoli

Milk production. The breasts produce thick yellow colostrum for the first few days after delivery. This contains antibodies against infection, so it is important that the baby gets it.

Once the placenta is delivered, its supply of oestrogen and progesterone stops. Low levels of these hormones stimulate prolactin secretion from the anterior pituitary, and this makes the breast milk flow freely within a few days of delivery. Growth hormone and thyroid hormones help.

Milk ejection. Oxytocin is released from the posterior pituitary in response to nerve impulses from the nipple when the baby sucks it, and also whenever the mother thinks about the baby. Oxytocin then makes the myoepithelial cells squeeze the milk in the alveoli onwards into the lactiferous ducts. This is the 'let-down reflex' and gives the prickling feeling of 'the milk coming in'.

Babies who suck the nipple and areola well into their mouths can compress the lactiferous sinuses with their mouths and tongues, thus pumping the let-down milk into their mouths.

Oxytocin also stimulates anterior pituitary hormones to maintain the milk supply, and makes the smooth muscle of the uterus contract, helping it to shrink to the non-pregnant size.

The Reproductive System and Daily Living

Sexual function involves:
— libido (sexual desire)
— potency (ability to have erections) in men
— lubrication and relaxation in women
— fertility (the ability to conceive or father children).

Sexual feelings are best expressed within a warm, loving relationship.
Sexual problems can poison the relationship, while a poor relationship can interfere with sexuality.
Patients discuss this aspect of their lives most easily with people who seem sensitive, open and who avoid hasty moral judgements.

Infertility can cause great unhappiness, as may an unplanned pregnancy.

The responsibilities of parenthood affect most activities of daily life. The work of parenting involves bending and lifting; this should be remembered when planning care, especially day surgery or an early discharge.